Instructor's Manual to accompany

INTRODUCTION TO

ORGANIC LABORATORY TECHNIQUES

Third Edition

Donald L. Pavia
Gary M. Lampman
George S. Kriz

Western Washington University
Bellingham, Washington

Saunders College Publishing
Harcourt Brace College Publishers
Fort Worth   Philadelphia   San Diego
New York   Orlando   Austin   San Antonio
Toronto   Montreal   London   Sydney   Tokyo

Printed in the United States of America

Instructor's Manual to accompany INTRODUCTION TO ORGANIC LAB TECHNIQUES, 3/e.

ISBN # 0-03-014814-6

3 4 5 6 7 8 9 0 1 018 9 8 7 6 5 4 3 2

CONTENTS

Introduction to the Third Edition

New experiments have been added to the Third Edition. They include preparations of acetaminophen, dimedone, tetraphenylporphyrin and metalloporphyrins, benzalacetone, benzalacetophenone, and 1,4-diphenyl-1,3-butadienes. Several others have been revised to reduce the amounts of chemicals used (triphenylmethanol and benzoic acid), improve yields (hydroboration of styrene), change type of instrumentation used (kinetics of oxidation of alcohols) or introduce use of carbon 13 nmr (Friedel-Crafts acylation). A new isolation experiment, Carotenoids Pigments from Spinach, has been added. In addition, a chiral shift reagent has been used to determine the optical purity of α-phenylethylamine.

This instructor's manual is intended to assist instructors, teaching assistants, and persons preparing materials for organic chemistry laboratory classes. An attempt is made to indicate the manner in which the authors envision the textbook might be used.

The list of chemicals and equipment required for each experiment are based on the amount required for ten students. For chemicals, the amounts indicated include at least 25% excess, to account for spillage or other types of waste.

The time required for each experiment is given in laboratory periods. It is assumed that a laboratory period is about three to four hours in length. For laboratory periods which are either shorter or longer, appropriate adjustments must be made.

Towards the end of this instructor's manual, the authors have included some sample laboratory schedules. These schedules are based on actual laboratory class schedules which have been used with the textbook. It should be pointed out that many of the techniques such as filtration, crystallization, melting point determination, extraction, and chromatography are most conveniently introduced by means of the isolation experiments. It should also be pointed out that the sample laboratory schedules illustrate the manner in which choices of experiments may be introduced. The authors have found that providing a class with choices of experiments increases student interest, since comparisons can be made among experiments.

It should be made clear that the technique sections of the textbook are designed to stand quite independently from the experiments. Instructors who have some favorite experiments may substitute them quite easily for those experiments which are contained in the textbook, and they may still take advantage of the technique discussion which are included in the textbook without having to rewrite them.

The authors have continued their effort in improving the safety of the experiments and the environment for students working in the laboratory. The nature of the study of chemical hazards is in such rapid flux, however, that the instructors must stay abreast of the latest developments in the field. The practice of strict control of hazardous waste is maintained, with instructions being given for the safe disposal of organic solvents and toxic metals.

Finally, the authors wish to thank a number of people who have sent corrections and suggestions that have been included in this new edition.

LABORATORY EQUIPMENT AND SUPPLIES

A. Individual student glassware and equipment contained in locker

1. Organic Chemistry Kit (19/22 joints)

   500 mL 3-Neck round bottom flask
   250 mL Round bottom flask with side tubulation
   25, 50, and 100 mL Round bottom boiling flasks
   Stoppers (two)
   Thermometer adapter
   Rubber thermometer holder
   Bleed tube (ebulliator tube)
   Claisen head
   Distilling head
   Vacuum adapter
   Condenser
   Fractionating column (packed with steel wool)
   125 mL Separatory funnel, Teflon stopcock

2. Other glassware

   Bent adapter
   Beakers; 50 mL (2), 100 mL (2), 250 mL (2),
            400 mL (1)
   Graduated cylinders; 10 mL and 100 mL
   Drying tubes (2)
   Evaporating dish, size 00
   Erlenmeyer flasks; 25 mL (2), 50 mL (2),
            125 mL (1), 250 mL (1), 500 mL (1)
   Filter flasks; 125 mL and 500 mL
   Separatory funnel, 500 mL (optional)
   Aspirator trap bottle
   Stemless funnel, 45 mm
   Powder funnel
   Hirsch funnel, size 000 (optional)
   Buchner funnels; size 0 and 2A
   Test tubes; 10 x 75 mm (12); 15 x 125 mm (6)
   Side arm test tube, 20 x 150 mm
   Thermometers; 250° and 360°
   Watch glasses; 50 mm (2) and 100 mm (2)
   Small ground glass bottles (6)
   4 oz. Screw cap bottles (2)
   Thiele melting point tube (optional)

3. Equipment

>   Dropper bulbs (6)
>   Neoprene adapters, nos. 2, 3, and 4
>   Polyethylene bottle, 8 oz.
>   Brushes, small and large
>   Micro burner and chimney
>   Condenser clamp with holder
>   Utility clamps (2)
>   Test tube clamp
>   Screw clamp
>   Wire gauze
>   Spatula
>   Test tube block
>   Rubber tubing
>   Pressure tubing
>   Scorer or file
>   Safety glasses

B. Community Equipment
    The following equipment should be available in the
    laboratory or nearby.

>   Ring stands
>   Iron rings
>   Steam baths
>   Ice buckets
>   Variable transformers
>   Heating mantle or oil baths
>   Hot plates
>   Electric melting point apparatus
>   Top-loading balances
>   Refractometer
>   Polarimeter
>   Centrifuge
>   Gas Chromatograph
>   Infrared Spectrometer
>   Potassium bromide mini-press
>   Salt plates
>   Solution cells
>   Ovens
>   Glass working bench with oxygen-methane torch
>   Cork borers
>   Scissors

Handbook of Chemistry and Physics (mounted on
board)
Handbook of Tables for Organic Compound
Identification (mounted on board)

C.   Community Supplies

1.   Chemicals and supplies
The following materials should be available at
all times on the side shelves or desks.

Boiling stones
Applicator sticks
Decolorizing carbon (Norit)
Corks, assorted
Sample vials for submitting products
Glass tubing
Glass rod
Filter paper for suction and gravity filtra-
tions
Stopcock grease
pH paper (Hydrion paper A and B)
Red and blue litmus paper
Glycerol in dropper bottle
Copper wire
Melting point capillary tubes
Glass wool
Cotton
Labels
Matches
Wooden blocks
Soap
Sponge
Mineral oil or bath oil
Celite (Filter Aid)
Rock salt
Anhydrous magnesium sulfate
Anhydrous calcium chloride
Anhydrous sodium sulfate

2.   Acids and bases
The solutions and reagents should be placed in
one area of the laboratory on a chemically
resistant surface.

Sodium hydroxide solutions; 5%, 2 $\underline{M}$, 25%
Saturated sodium carbonate solution
Sodium bicarbonate solution, 5%
Hydrochloric acid solutions; concentrated, 6 $\underline{N}$,
     5%, 10%
Sodium chloride solution, saturated
Nitric acid, concentrated
Ammonium hydroxide, concentrated
Sulfuric acid, concentrated

3. Common solvents
These solvents should be placed in a hood during use and stored in a special cabinet at other times (see below).

Petroleum ether (Ligroin)
Acetone
Methanol
Toluene
Methylene chloride
95% Ethanol
Ether
Carbon tetrachloride (1 pt), kept in a hood
     near the infrared spectrometer, with
     an eye dropper attached.

4. Test reagent shelves
We usually keep the reagents and known compounds for Experiment 56 (qualitative analysis) in a designated area of the laboratory at all times. The noxious chemicals are kept in a hood.

D. Safety

Storage cabinet for flammable organic solvents
Fire extinguishers
Eye wash fountains
Showers
Fire blankets
Solutions for acid and base burns: 5% sodium
     bicarbonate and 5% acetic acid solutions
Solvent waste containers
Heavy metal waste containers (i.e. chromium waste)

E.　Safety References

R. E. Lenga, ed. <u>The Sigma-Aldrich Library of Chemical Safety Data</u>. Milwaukee : Sigma-Aldrich Corp., 1985.

N. I. Sax and R. J. Lewis, Sr., ed. <u>Rapid Guide to Hazardous Chemicals in the Work Place</u>. New York : Van Nostrand Reinhold Co., 1986.

<u>Prudent Practices for Disposal of Chemicals from Laboratories</u>. Washington, D. C. : National Academy Press, 1983.

<u>Prudent Practices for Handling Hazardous Chemicals in Laboratories</u>. Washington, D. C. : National Academy Press, 1981.

R. E. Gosselin, R. P. Smith and H. C. Hodge. <u>Clinical Toxicology of Commercial Products</u>. 5th ed. Baltimore : Williams and Wilkins, 1984.

<u>Fire Protection Guide on Hazardous Materials</u>. 9th ed. Quincy, MA : National Fire Protection Association, 1986.

<u>Safety in Academic Chemistry Laboratories</u>. 4th ed. Washington, D.C. : American Chemical Society, 1985.

M. M. Renfrew, ed. <u>Safety in the Chemical Laboratory</u>, Vol IV. Easton, PA : J. Chem. Ed. ACS, 1981. See also continuing series of articles in monthly issues of J. Chem. Ed.; <u>Safety in the Chemical Laboratory</u> by M. M. Renfrew, editor.

<u>The Merck Index</u>. 10th ed. Rahway, NJ : Merck and Co., 1983.

Experiment 1

ACETYLSALICYLIC ACID

TIME ESTIMATE: 2 periods

CHEMICALS PER 10 STUDENTS:

Salicylic acid   25 g
Acetic anhydride   60 mL
1% (by weight) Aqueous ferric chloride solution
    1g/ 100 mL water   ca. 100 mL
                              (in a dropper bottle)

Saturated aqueous sodium bicarbonate solution 350 mL
    6.9g/ 100 mL water
Ethyl acetate
Potassium iodide solution   ca. 100 mL
                                (in a dropper bottle)
    0.25 g iodine, 0.5 g potassium iodide, and 10
    mL of water are mixed. This solution is
    diluted ten-fold for use. The solution should
    be straw-colored in appearance.
Phenol   1 g
Aspirin tablets
Sulfuric acid (concentrated)   (in dropper bottle)
Hydrochloric acid (concentrated)
Petroleum ether (30-60°)

ANSWERS TO QUESTIONS:

1.   The sulfuric acid acts as a catalyst in the acetylation
reaction. Acetic anhydride reacts with salicylic acid too
slowly for a practical reaction. However, protonating the
carbonyl group oxygen of the acetic anhydride increases the
electron-deficient nature of the carbonyl group. Salicylic
acid's hydroxyl group, acting as a nucleophile, can attack
this protonated group more easily.

2.   The polymeric by-product might be represented by the
structure.

3.   The polymeric by-product does not possess a free carboxyl group which can be ionized by the basic bicarbonate ion. The by-product, therefore, does not dissolve in aqueous solution. Furthermore, the very high molecular weight of the polymer also reduces its solubility.

4.   The yield of acetylsalicylic acid, starting with 5.0 g of salicylic acid and an excess of acetic anhydride, would be:

Molecular weights: salicylic acid = 138.1
                    acetylsalicylic acid = 180.2

5.0 g salicylic acid = $\dfrac{5.0}{138.1}$ = 0.036 moles salicylic acid

Theoretical yield of acetylsalicylic acid
                        = 0.036 moles
                        = (0.036) (180.2)
                        = 6.52 g

5.   When heated in boiling water, aspirin decomposes to give salicylic acid and acetic acid. The salicylic acid, with its free phenolic hydroxyl group, produces a ferric chloride test.

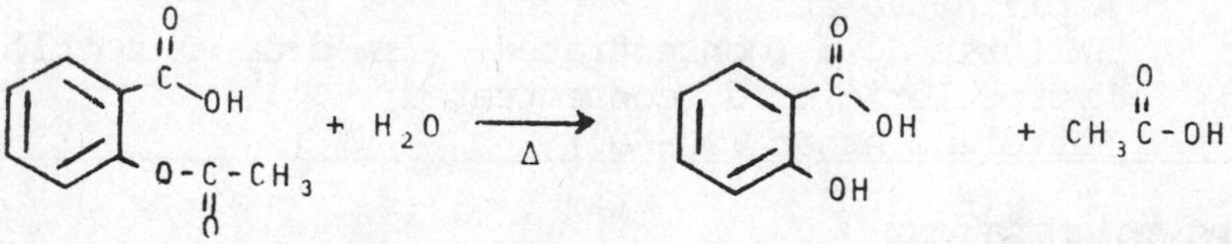

Experiment 2

ACETANILIDE

TIME ESTIMATE: 1 to 2 periods (Two periods if done near the beginning of the year).

CHEMICALS PER 10 STUDENTS:

Aniline (technical grade)   25 g
    Crude, highly colored aniline is more effective for this experiment, since it dramatically shows the

10

effect of decolorization by charcoal.

Acetic anhydride	35 mL
Activated charcoal	8 g

ANSWERS TO QUESTIONS:

1.   Aniline has a free $-NH_2$ group. The electron pairs on the nitrogen atom are available for coordination with electron-deficient reagents, making the group basic. Acetanilide does not have a free $-NH_2$ group; rather it has an acetamido group, $-NHCOCH_3$.   Resonance interaction between the electron pair on nitrogen and the carbonyl group make the electron pair less available for sharing. Consequently, the group is much less basic than an $-NH_2$ group.

2.   The theoretical yield of acetanilide, starting with 10.0g of aniline and an excess of acetic anhydride, would be:

Molecular weights: aniline = 93.1
                              acetanilide = 135.2

10.0 g aniline $- \dfrac{10.0}{93.1} = $ 0.107 moles

Theoretical yield of acetanilide   = 0.107 moles
                                                = (0.107) (135.2)
                                                = 14.5 g

3.   Reactions of aniline with acetyl chloride and acetic acid to give acetanilide:

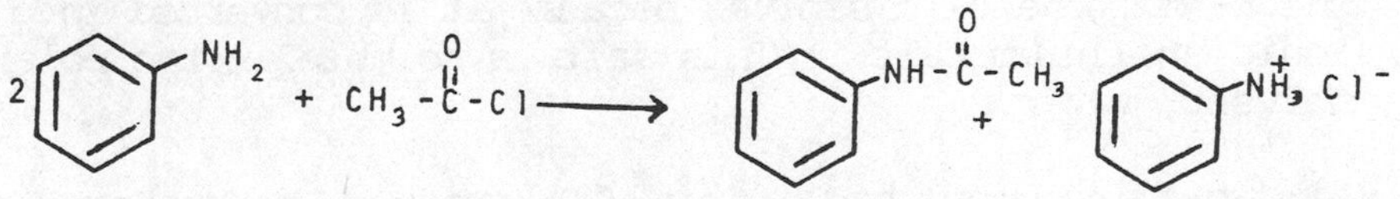

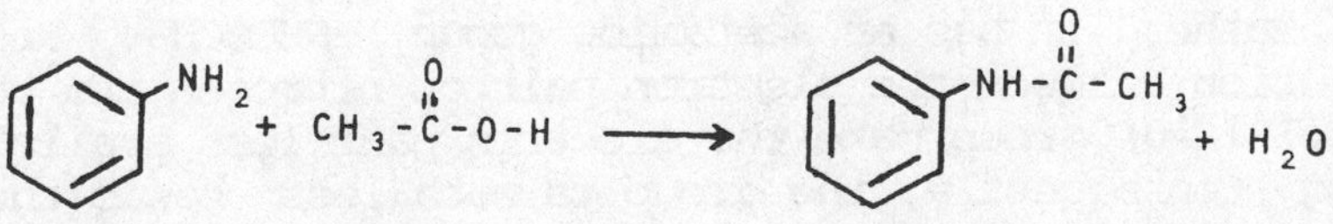

4. The hydrolysis of acetic anhydride:

$$CH_3-\overset{\overset{O}{\|}}{C}-O-\overset{\overset{O}{\|}}{C}-CH_3 \ + \ H_2O \longrightarrow \ 2 \ CH_3-\overset{\overset{O}{\|}}{C}-OH$$

Experiment 3

ACETAMINOPHEN

TIME ESTIMATE: 1 to 2 periods (Two periods if done near the beginning of the year).

CHEMICALS PER 10 STUDENTS:

P-Aminophenol	25 g
Acetic anhydride	25 mL
Sodium acetate tri hydrate	30 g
Activated charcoal	8 g
Hydrochloric acid (concentrated)	25 mL

ANSWERS TO QUESTIONS:

1.

The p-Aminophenol dissolves because it is converted into an ionic anilinium salt.   This salt is soluble in the polar solvent, water.

2.   p-Aminophenol has a free $-NH_2$ group. The unshared pairs of electrons on the nitrogen atom are available for coordination with electron-deficient reagents, such as protons making the group basic. Acetaminophen does not have a free $-NH_2$ group; rather, it has an acetamido group, $-NHCOCH_3$. Resonance interaction between the electron pair on nitrogen and the carbonyl (C=O) group make the electron pair less available for sharing. Consequently, the group is much less basic than an $-NH_2$ group.

12

3. A proposed preparation of phenacetin

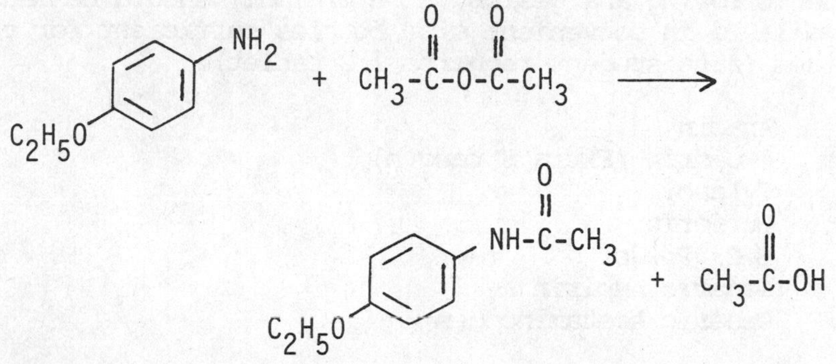

4. The theoretical yield of acetaminophen, starting with 10.0 g of p-Aminophenol and an excess of acetic anhydride would be:

Molecular weights: p-aminophenol = 109.1
acetaminophen = 151.2

$$10.0 \text{ g p-aminophenol} = \frac{10.0}{109.1} = 0.092 \text{ moles}$$

Theoretical yield of acetaminophen = 0.092 moles
= (0.092) (151.2)
= 13.9 g

Experiment 4

TLC ANALYSIS OF ANALGESIC DRUGS

TIME ESTIMATE: One period, or less

This experiment may be co-scheduled with another shorter experiment, or during the continuation of a longer one. Students may work individually or, alternatively, the experiment may be performed by students working in pairs, one student preparing the tlc slide of the reference substances, and one student preparing the tlc slide of the unknowns.

13

CHEMICALS AND SUPPLIES:

The following analgesics (at a minimum) should be made available in convenient size bottles sufficient for the class (each student requires 1/2 tablet):

    Anacin
    Excedrin (Extra Strength)
    Tylenol
    Bufferin
    B.C. Powder
    Generic Aspirin
    Generic Acetaminophen

APC tablets are no longer available, and we have eliminated phenacetin from the third edition of the book. Since the compositions of analgesic drugs are continuously being changed, you should look at the label to be sure of the composition. Salicylamide containing drugs are becoming hard to find; B.C. Powder still has it. An instructor may need to supply the students with a mixture of known composition.

Small bottles containing solutions of each of the following chemicals dissolved in 50/50 CH_2Cl_2/EtOH (1 g per 20 mL of mixed solvent except aspirin, for which 0.5 g is recommend) will be required:

    4'-Hydroxyacetanilide (acetaminophen)   MCB HX660 (100 g)
    Aspirin (acetylsalicylic acid)   MCB AX225 (500 g)
    Caffeine   MCB CX80   (100 g)
    Salicylamide   MCB SX50   (250 g)

In addition, 20 mL of a combined standard reference mixture of all four compounds at the same concentrations is required. Use a steam bath for gentle heating where necessary.

These solutions should be made up immediately prior to the laboratory period since they are not stable over long periods. The aspirin, for instance, will solvolyze quite soon. In fact, if excessive tailing of the aspirin spot is observed on the tlc slides, this may be due to partial decomposition of the aspirin sample either by solvolysis or by hydrolysis due to exposure to water or to moist air. The solutions are adequate for any size class.

The following additional supplies are required:

Eastman Chromatogram Sheets with Fluorescent indicator
(Eastman No. 13181, box of 20 sheets)

Each sheet is cut into six 10 cm x
6.6 cm slides. Thus one large
sheet will suffice for 3 students
working individually, or for 6
students working in pairs.

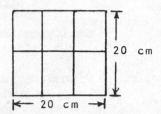

A hand-held UV lamp
We prefer:

Mineralight UVSL-25, 4 Watt long and short wave-
length uv light (Ultraviolet Products, Inc., 5100
Walnut Grove Avenue, San Gabriel, CA 91778).
Available from most chemical supply houses.

Thin wall open end capillary tubing (1 mm) for micropipets

Filter paper, squares to prepare liners

32 oz. wide mouth, screw cap jars (Mason jars will work)

Iodine (small amounts in several 32 oz. developing jars)

Development solvents:

Ethyl acetate is recommended (see also alternates
mentioned in experiment.)

Solvents for preparing the samples to be spotted:

Methylene chloride and ethanol

INSTRUCTIONS FOR SPECIAL EQUIPMENT OR REAGENT HANDLING:

We prefer to set aside one area in the laboratory (two
areas in a large lab section) for spotting the tlc slides. A
large piece of butcher paper is spread out on the desk and the
bottles of standards, the analgesics, the tlc slides, and the
development jars are all placed in this clean, organized area.
One hood is darkened by taping either butcher paper or
aluminum foil over its glass cover. The uv lamp is placed in
this hood. Alternatively, a large, upside-down cardboard box

15

could be used (with appropriate holes cut); or, if a small side room which can be darkened is available, it can be used.

SPECIAL NOTES:

The approximate order of elution is:

Salicylamide (fluoresces) > Acetaminophen > Aspirin > Caffeine

Visualization with iodine:
Salicylamide and acetaminophen produce dark spots. Caffeine produces a light spot. Aspirin does not produce a spot.

Experiment 5

NICOTINE FROM TOBACCO

TIME ESTIMATE: 1 to 2 periods (Two periods if done near the beginning of the year.)

CHEMICALS AND SUPPLIES PER 10 STUDENTS:

10 Old dry cigars (one per student)
Buy these well in advance, unwrap them, and allow them to dry in the air. Alternatively, you may be able to obtain old cigars from a tobacconist or a distributor.

5% Aqueous sodium hydroxide solution   1250 mL

Ether, solvent grade   1000 mL

Methanol   125 mL

Saturated methanolic picric acid   125 mL

Boiling methanol dissolves an unbelievable amount of picric acid, most of which crystallizes on cooling. Use some caution in amounts, and then decant the cooled solution from any crystals which form. Solutions should be freshly prepared, and care should be taken to avoid contamination with metals. Picrates of lead, iron, zinc, nickel, copper, etc. are

16

very dangerous, and may explode when heated with
picric acid. Excess solutions should be poured into
water for storage and disposal. Students should
pour their filtrates into a sink, rather than into a
waste container to avoid the possibility of coming
into contact with heavy metal waste.

Pine applicator sticks (1 box)

Fast filter paper (E and D 617, S and S 595 or WHATMAN 1)

Ethanol

SPECIAL NOTES:

Do not heat the tobacco-sodium hydroxide solution or
attempt to use a stronger solution in the hopes of improving the yield of nicotine. Anything other then this
mild, room temperature treatment will destroy the
nicotine.

ANSWERS TO QUESTIONS:
1.

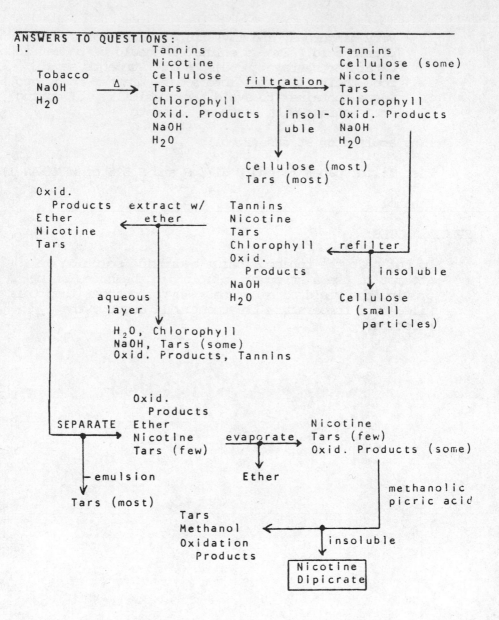

18

2.

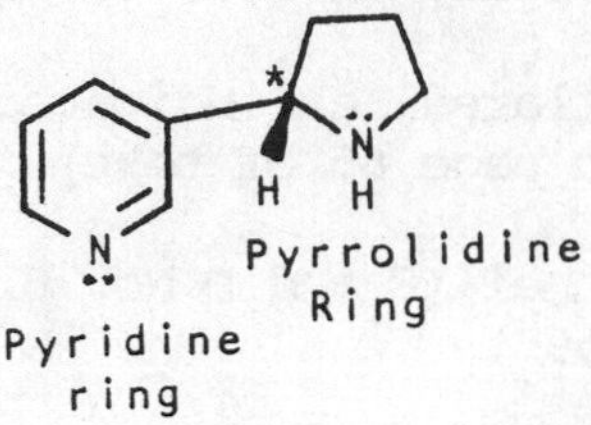

They pyrrolidine ring is more basic mainly due to its hybridization. In pyridine, the nitrogen atom is sp^2 hybridized, in pyrrolidine it is sp^3 hybridized. The sp^3 hybrided orbitals have less s character (which destablizes the unshared electrons) and are, hence, more basic.

Pyridine ring

Pyrrolidine Ring

3.   See the answer given to question 3 in Experiment 6.

4.   See the answer given to question 4 in Experiment 6.

5.   See the asterisk in the structure above.

Experiment 6

ISOLATION OF CAFFEINE FROM TEA

TIME ESTIMATE: 2 periods

CHEMICALS AND SUPPLIES FOR 10 STUDENTS:

Dry tea leaves   310 g (3/4 pound)
    Buy loose tea of the cheapest type possible. Tea bags are more expensive, and they omit practice in the filtration techniques. Instant tea may also be used with the same criticism. A lesser amount of instant tea, about 20 g, should be used.

Calcium carbonate, powder   125 g

Magnesium sulfate (anhyd.)   25 g

Methylene chloride   1250 mL

Acetone   125 mL

Petroleum ether (30-60°)   125 mL

Cotton

15 x 125 mm Test tubes (if not already in drawer)

20 x 150 mm sidearm test tubes (flared, as indicated in
footnote 2 on page 65 of text)

Fast filter paper for Buchner funnel (E and D No. 617 or
S and S No. 595)

Derivative (optional)

Salicylic acid	3 g
Toluene	50 mL
Petroleum Ether (30-90°)	15 mL

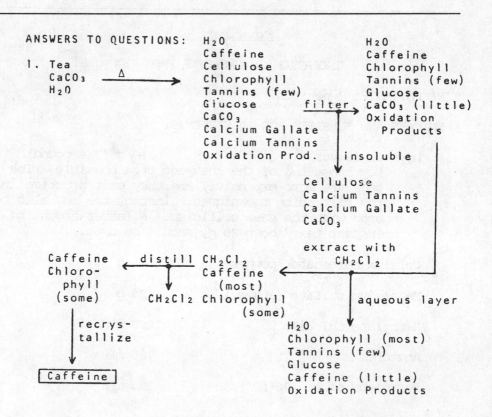

ANSWERS TO QUESTIONS:

1. Tea
   CaCO₃   Δ
   H₂O

H₂O
Caffeine
Cellulose
Chlorophyll
Tannins (few)
Glucose
CaCO₃
Calcium Gallate
Calcium Tannins
Oxidation Prod.

filter

H₂O
Caffeine
Chlorophyll
Tannins (few)
Glucose
CaCO₃ (little)
Oxidation
Products

insoluble

Cellulose
Calcium Tannins
Calcium Gallate
CaCO₃

extract with
CH₂Cl₂

Caffeine
Chloro-
  phyll
(some)

distill

CH₂Cl₂

CH₂Cl₂
Caffeine
(most)
Chlorophyll
(some)

aqueous layer

recrys-
tallize

H₂O
Chlorophyll (most)
Tannins (few)
Glucose
Caffeine (little)
Oxidation Products

Caffeine

2.

Nitrogen no. 4 is the most basic for the following reasons. Both nitrogens nos. 1 and 2 are amide nitrogens. They are conjugated with the carbonyl groups. The conjugation decreases the basicity. Nitrogen no. 3 has its unshared pair of electrons as a part of a $4n+2$ $(n=1)$ pi electron aromatic ring system; thus, the basicity of nitrogen no. 3 is also reduced by conjugation.

The unshared pair of electrons on nitrogen no. 4 cannot participate in the ring resonance. It is in an sp^2 hybrid orbital which is oriented perpendicularly (orthogonally) to the aromatic pi system. These electrons cannot participate in any sort of resonance and are, therefore, the most available, making nitrogen no. 4 the most basic of all the nitrogen atoms.

3. All the hydroxyl groups of the digalloyl groups are phenolic and, hence, acidic. The para hydroxyl groups should be the most acidic due to the extra resonance involving the carbonyl groups that can be accomplished in the conjugate base. The meta hydroxyls cannot involve this carbonyl group in resonance stabilization in the conjugate base forms.

etc.

4. Tannic acid could be hydrolyzed by either acid (best) or basic hydrolysis. The gallic acid thus formed could be separarated from glucose by making the solution strongly acidic and then extracting with ether. The gallic acid would extract into ether from the low pH solution, wherein it would exist in its neutral, protonated form.

5. The petroleum ether (ligroin) was added to precipitate the caffeine. It decreases the polarity of the solution.

6. Water codistills with methylene chloride as an azeotrope. When the distillate cools, water separates to yield a cloudy solution.

7. The ionic magnesium sulfate makes the aqueous and organic layers less compatible because it dissolves to some extent in the water, so that the layers separate from each other. In addition, the small amount of water present is removed because magnesium sulfate is a drying agent.

8. A small amount of chlorophyll is present in the isolated caffeine giving it a greenish tinge.

Experiment 7

ISOLATION OF CAFFEINE FROM COFFEE

TIME ESTIMATE: 2 periods

CHEMICALS AND SUPPLIES PER 10 STUDENTS:

Ground Coffee (Regular Grind)   1 lb (454 g)
   Instant coffee may be used, but the practice gained from the original filtration would be omitted. A lesser amount of instant coffee should be used (Ca. 20-25 g).

Calcium carbonate, powder   125 g

Magnesium sulfate (anhyd.)   175 g

Methylene chloride   1250 mL

Acetone   125 mL

Petroleum ether (30-60°)   125 mL

Fast filter paper for Buchner funnel (E and D #617 or S and S #595)

Test tubes (see previous experiment)

Derivative (see previous experiment)

22

SPECIAL NOTES:

It is important to use a fast filter paper, such as those mentioned above to avoid clogging. It will be desirable to emphasize and demonstrate the correct manner of shaking and venting the separatory funnel to avoid difficulties with emulsions.

ANSWER TO QUESTIONS:

1.   The separation will be similar to that given in the previous experiment (Caffeine from Tea), except that fats (waxes), furfurals and chlorogenic acid will be present in addition to those substances listed. The fats (waxes) and calcium chlorogenate should be removed in the first filtration (insoluble), while furfural will remain behind in the aqueous layer after the extraction with methylene chloride.

2.   The decaffeination process is conducted prior to roasting in order to avoid removal of the aromatic roasting products such as furfural, and also to allow for a complete removal of the organic solvent through heating during the roasting process.

3.   See answer to question 3 in Experiment 6.

4.   See answer to question 4 in Experiment 6.

5.   See answer to question 5 in Experiment 6.

6.   Chlorophyll and other substances undergo decomposition during the roasting process, resulting in a brown color. This colored impurity is carried through the isolation scheme and appears in the final isolated caffeine.

7.   See answer to question 6 in Experiment 6.

8.   See answer to question 7 in Experiment 6.

Experiment 8

CHOLESTEROL FROM GALLSTONES

TIME ESTIMATE: 2 periods

CHEMICALS PER 10 STUDENTS:

Gallstones   25 g
> These may be obtained from a hospital laboratory or a medical laboratory. They should be pulverized in a blender.

Brominating solution   65 mL (in a dropper bottle)
> 0.55 g anhydrous sodium acetate powder, 65 mL acetic acid, and 7.4 g Br_2 are mixed.

Zinc dust   2.5 g

Methanol   250 mL

Diethyl ether   500 mL

Acetic acid (concentrated)   150 mL

Saturated aqueous sodium chloride solution   2 L
> 31.7 g/100 mL water (stored in poly-ethylene bottle)

10% (by weight) Aqueous sodium hydroxide solution   2 L
> 10 g/90 mL water (stored in polyethyl-ene bottle)

ANSWERS TO QUESTIONS:

1. Cholesterol
    Bilirubin
    Cholestanol
    7-Dehydrocho-
      lesterol
    Δ⁷-Cholesten-
      3β-ol

    → dissolve →

    Cholesterol
    Cholestanol
    7-Dehydrocho-
      lesterol
    Δ⁷-Cholesten-
      3β-ol

    →

    insoluble

    ← bilirubin

    Br_2/acetic acid → Cholesterol
                         dibromide

    soluble
    in acetic
    acid

    Cholestanol
    7-Dehydrocholesterol
    Δ⁷-Cholesten-3β-ol

    $\xrightarrow[\text{acetic acid}]{Zn}$

    recrystallize
    from
    ether/methanol

    insol-
    uble

    $ZnBr_2$

    Cholesterol
    (pure)

2. Step 1:

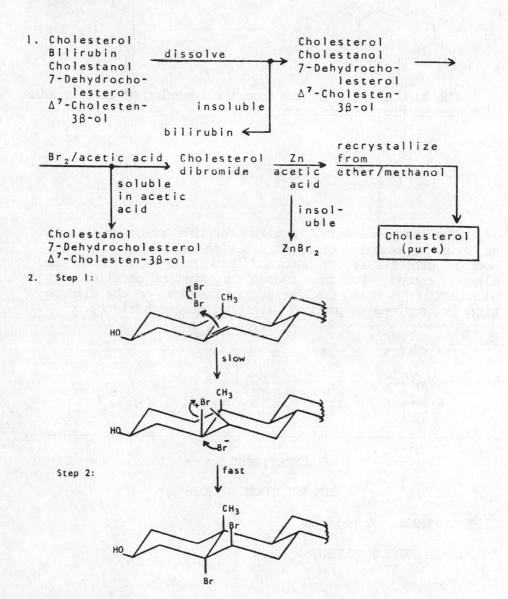

slow

Step 2:   fast

25

3.

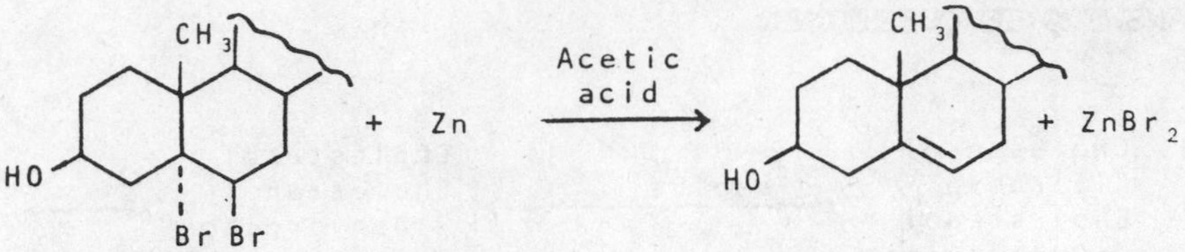

The zinc acetate arises from the reaction of zinc bromide with the acetic acid solvent.

4.

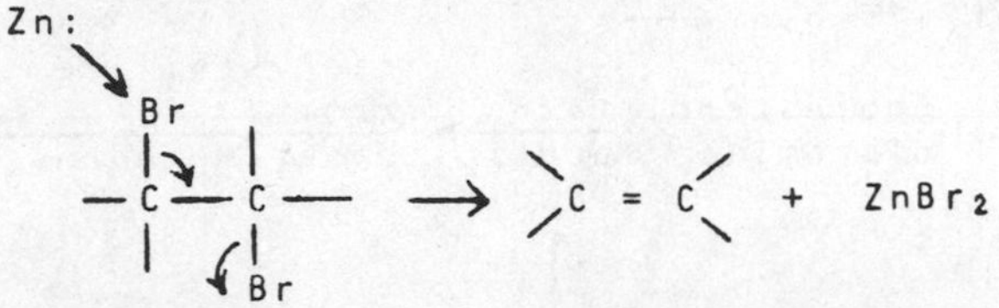

The stereochemistry required for this reaction is _anti_. As in other examples of E2 elimination reactions, the C-Br bonding orbitals are transformed into the p-orbitals of the alkene π-bond. For this reason they must be parallel. _Syn_ elimination is ruled out for steric reasons, so the elimination is required to proceed with _anti_ stereochemistry.

5.

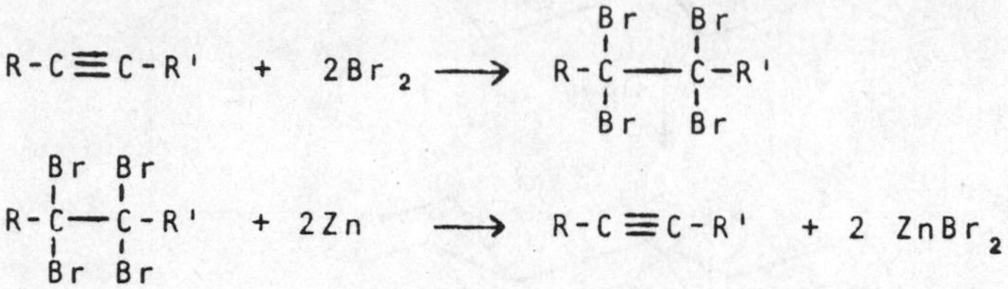

$$R-C \equiv C-R' \; + \; 2Br_2 \longrightarrow \; R-\underset{\underset{Br}{|}}{\overset{\overset{Br}{|}}{C}}-\underset{\underset{Br}{|}}{\overset{\overset{Br}{|}}{C}}-R'$$

$$R-\underset{\underset{Br}{|}}{\overset{\overset{Br}{|}}{C}}-\underset{\underset{Br}{|}}{\overset{\overset{Br}{|}}{C}}-R' \; + \; 2Zn \longrightarrow \; R-C \equiv C-R' \; + \; 2 \; ZnBr_2$$

Experiment 9

ETHANOL FROM SUCROSE

TIME ESTIMATE: 2 periods

CHEMICALS PER 10 STUDENTS:

Sucrose	500 g
Baker's yeast	5 packages dry yeast
	or 200 g cake yeast
Pasteur' salts	

26

2.0 g potassium phosphate, 0.2 g calcium phosphate, 0.2 g magnesium sulfate, and 10.0 g ammonium tartrate dissolved   in 860 mL water.

Celite   200 g

Saturated aqueous barium   250 mL
    hydroxide

    8.6 g/100 mL water

Kerosene or xylene   75 mL

Anhydrous potassium carbonate   500 g

OTHER APPARATUS REQUIRED:

500 mL Erlenmeyer flasks (if not   10

    included in locker equipment

Small bottles (if not included in   10

    locker equipment)

Glass tubing

ANSWERS TO QUESTIONS:

1.   Two possible methods:
a)   Obtain 95% ethanol from fermentation by distillation. Then add enough benzene to remove the water by means of the benzene-water-ethanol azeotrope (see pages 575-577) and redistill.

b) $CH_2=CH_2 + H_2SO_4 \longrightarrow CH_3-CH_2OSO_3H$

    $CH_3-CH_2-OSO_3H + H_2O \longrightarrow CH_3CH_2OH + H_2SO_4$

2.   The air trap is necessary to prevent air from reaching the fermentation mixture. In the presence of air, and with the

aid of certain bacteria, the ethanol may be oxidized to acetic acid.

3.   The density of pure ethanol is less than ethanol-water mixtures. By preparing standard solutions of known percentages of ethanol and water and by weighing known volumes of these solutions precisely, one may determine their densities. An unknown solution may be compared against these standard solutions by weighing a known volume precisely. The density of the unknown solution may thus be determined.

4.   The acetaldehyde impurity results from the slow air oxidation of ethanol.

5.   Diethylacetal arise from the reaction of ethanol with a trace amount of acetaldehyde impurity (see above).

$$CH_3-\overset{\overset{\displaystyle O}{\|}}{C}-H \ + \ 2 \ CH_3CH_2OH \ \longrightarrow \ CH_3-\overset{\overset{\displaystyle OCH_2CH_3}{|}}{\underset{\underset{\displaystyle OCH_2CH_3}{|}}{C}}-H \qquad + \ H_2O$$

6. $C_{12}H_{22}O_{11} \ + \ H_2O \ \longrightarrow \ 4 \ C_2H_5OH \ + \ 4 \ CO_2$

Molec. weight: $C_{12}H_{22}O_{11} \ = \ 342.30$

40 g sucrose $= \ \dfrac{40 \ g}{342.30 \ g/mole} \ = \ 0.12$ moles sucrose

0.12 moles sucrose $= \ (4)(0.12) \ = \ 0.48$ moles CO_2

$\dfrac{0.48}{1} \ = \ \dfrac{X}{22400}$; $X \ = $ mL CO_2 at STP

$X \ = \ 10750$ mL CO_2

$\dfrac{10750}{273} \ = \ \dfrac{V}{298}$; $V \ = $ mL CO_2 at 25 C

$V \ = \ 11700$ mL CO_2
_____

Experiment 10

ISOPENTYL ACETATE (BANANA OIL)

TIME ESTIMATE: One period

CHEMICALS AND SUPPLIES PER 10 STUDENTS:

Isopentyl alcohol (3-methyl-1-butanol)	165 mL (136 g)
Glacial acetic acid	225 mL (230 g)
Conc. H_2SO_4	50 mL
5% Aqueous $NaHCO_3$	1200 mL
Sat'd aqueous NaCl solution 31.7 g/100 mL water (stored in polyethylene bottle)	75 mL
Anhydrous magnesium sulfate	50 g

SPECIAL NOTES:

This experiment may be stopped just before the distillation. The ester should be left stored over anhyd. $MgSO_4$ in a tightly stoppered container (no rubber stoppers!). A longer reflux period may give a better yield, but is not necessary. We often assign another short experiment to be done simultaneously (i.e., thin layer chromatography). This allows students to keep busy during the reflux period. When scheduled this way two periods should be allowed.

ANSWERS TO QUESTIONS:

1.

All steps
equilibria

2. a) Remove water as it is formed.
    b) Remove product as it is formed.

Although not involving the right hand side of the
equation, it is also possible to add an excess of the alcohol.

3.

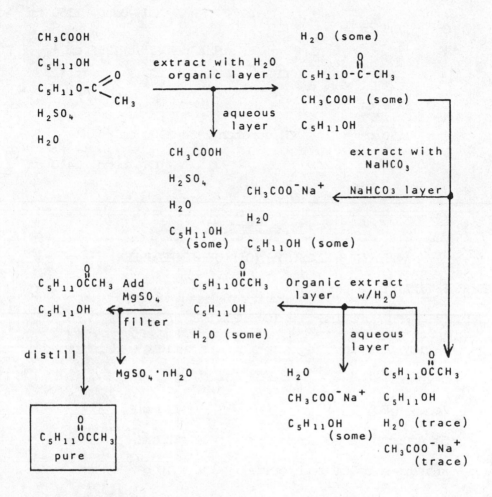

4. Excess acetic acid is easier to remove because of its high solubility in water. It can simply be extracted into water.

5.   gem dimethyl:

CH_3 bend   1350 cm^{-1}

C=O   1705 cm^{-1}

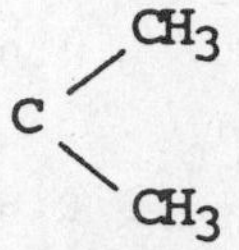

$$C \begin{matrix} \diagup CH_3 \\ \diagdown CH_3 \end{matrix}$$

split peaks at 1350 cm^{-1}

C-O   1210 cm^{-1}

1030 cm^{-1} CH stretch 2800-2900 cm^{-1}

CH_2 bend   1440 cm^{-1}

Experiment 11

METHYL SALICYLATE (OIL OF WINTERGREEN)

TIME ESTIMATE: 2 periods

CHEMICALS AND SUPPLIES FOR 10 STUDENTS:

Salicylic acid	110 g
Methanol	275 mL
Conc. H_2SO_4	110 mL
5% Aqueous $NaHCO_3$	625 mL
Anhydrous calcium chloride	10 g
Boiling stones	
Manometers	
Y-tubes	

SPECIAL NOTES:

This experiment requires a long period of reflux (1 hour). Another shorter experiment can be performed simultaneously to keep students busy during this period of reflux. If the condenser from the organic kit is required for the simultaneous experiment, the packing can be removed from the

32

fractional distillation column to afford a second condenser.
Since the experiment requires a vacuum distillation, it may be
more efficient to divide the class into two halves, one half
doing this experiment, and the other half performing another
experiment. Following this, the two halves of the class can
perform whichever experiment was missed in the prior peri-
od(s). This arrangement eases the demands on water line pressure from the aspirators and avoids floods due to overloaded
drains.

Another arrangement which relieves aspirator "pressure"
is to have students perform the vacuum distillation in groups
of two or three. If students are required to perform the distillation individually, the experiment should be scaled up to
give more product per student (a scaling factor of 2-3).

Several manometers should be available to check the
vacuum distillation apparatus for leaks and so that each student can utilize the manometer for at least a portion of the
distillation. The experiment specifies a hook-up procedure
for the manometer which allows it to be removed once reduced
pressure is established, measured, and stabilized.

ANSWERS TO QUESTIONS:

1.

$$+ H\text{-}OSO_3H$$

$$HSO_4^- +$$

$$CH_3\text{-}\ddot{O}\text{-}H$$

$$H\text{-}OSO_3H \qquad HSO_4^-$$

$$+ H_2SO_4$$
$$+ HSO_4^-$$

33

2. The sulfuric acid in this reaction is a catalyst and is not consumed (see mechanism above).

3. a) Excess of salicylic acid
   b) Remove water
   c) Remove product

4. Sulfuric acid and excess methanol are removed by extraction with water; both are soluble.

5. a) $NaHCO_3$ was used to remove unreacted salicylic acid and the catalyst H_2SO_4:

$$H_2SO_4 + NaHCO_3 \longrightarrow Na_2SO_4 + H_2O + CO_2$$

   b) Sodium hydroxide is a stronger base. Although it would have also removed the unreacted salicylic acid, it may have presented a danger of hydrolysis of the product.

See, for example, Experiment 12.

34

6. Infrared:

Phenolic OH 3200 cm^{-1} C=O 1675 cm^{-1}
    Internally H-bonded

CH stretch
    (Shoulder on OH) $2800-$ Low due to conjuga-
    3100 cm^{-1} tion and internal H-
                            bonding:

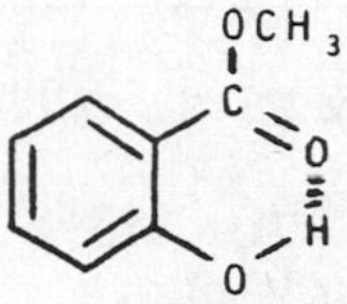

C-O several bands
    $1000-1400$ cm^{-1}

Aromatic C=C
    Two doublets 1600 & 1450 cm^{-1}

CH out of plane bending
    $600-900$ cm^{-1}
    o-substitution

NMR:

    3.8δ -OCH$_3$ 10.8δ -OH
                                    Shifted way downfield
    $6.5 - 7.8\delta$ aromatic ring   by internal H-bonding
                 protons   (see above)

Experiment 12

HYDROLYSIS OF METHYL SALICYLATE

TIME ESTIMATE: 1 period

CHEMICALS AND SUPPLIES PER 10 STUDENTS:

NaOH pellets   125 g

Methyl salicylate   65 g
    (may be student-prepared: Experiment 11)

1M Aqueous H$_2$SO$_4$ 2 L

Blue litmus paper

35

SPECIAL NOTES:

This is a simple experiment requiring few techniques that provides a beautiful answer as to what to do with all the student-prepared methyl salicylate produced from Experiment 11. It can be scheduled as an early experiment. Alternatively Experiments 11 and 12 may be assigned sequentially. This experiment is a good one for introducing crystallization.

ANSWERS TO QUESTIONS:

1. The white solid which forms is the sodium salt of methyl salicylate.

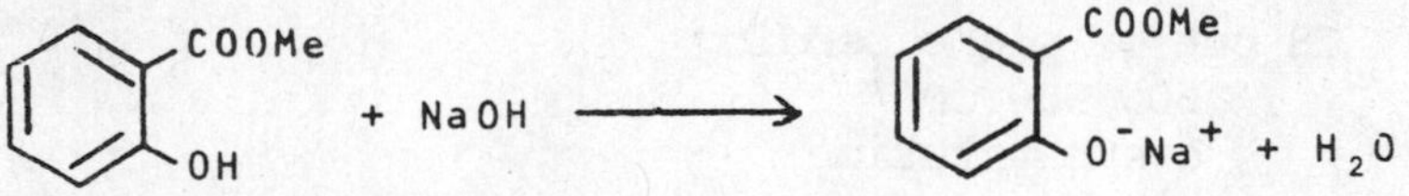

(benzene ring with COOMe and OH substituents) + NaOH $\longrightarrow$ (benzene ring with COOMe and O^-Na^+ substituents) + H_2O

It subsequently redissolves on heating.

2.

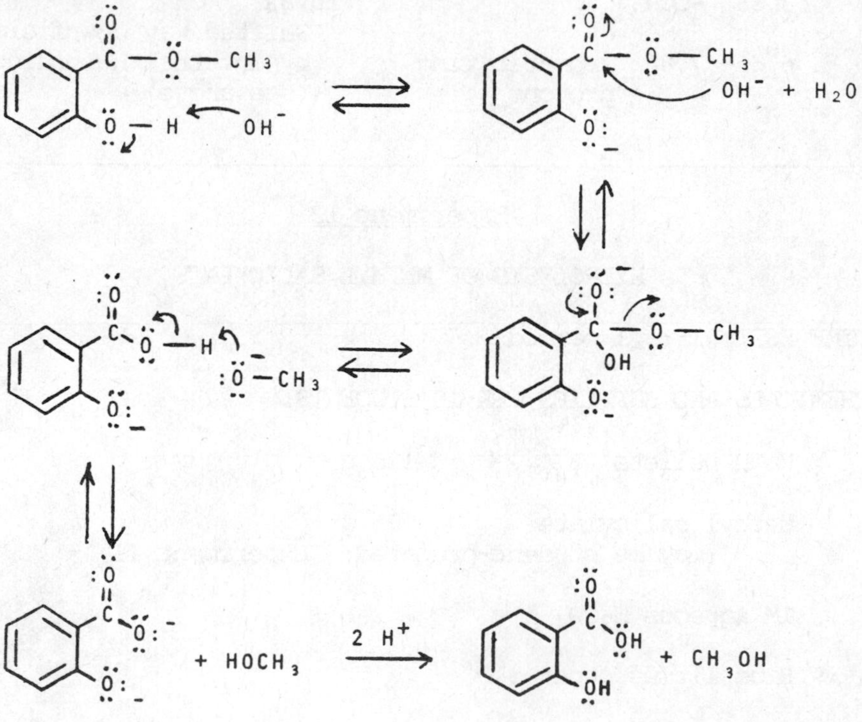

(reaction mechanism scheme showing base-catalyzed ester hydrolysis of methyl salicylate through tetrahedral intermediates, producing the salicylate dianion + CH_3OH, followed by protonation)

$+ \ HOCH_3 \quad \xrightarrow{2\ H^+} \quad$ (salicylic acid) $+ \ CH_3OH$

36

3. Sodium hydroxide is consumed:

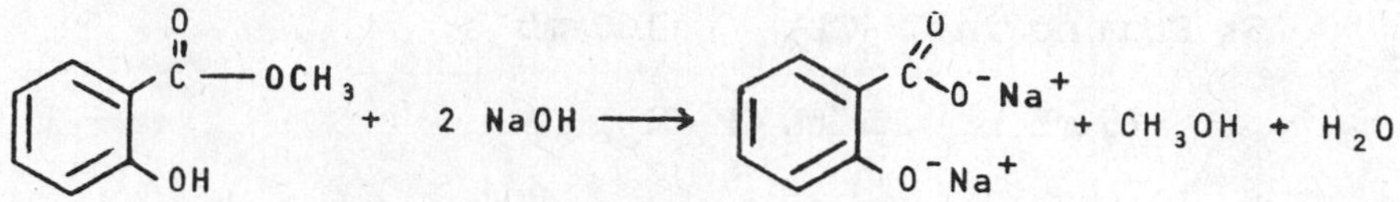

$$\text{(methyl salicylate)} + 2\ NaOH \longrightarrow \text{(disodium salt)} + CH_3OH + H_2O$$

Experiment 13

METHYL STEARATE FROM METHYL OLEATE

TIME ESTIMATE: 1 period

CHEMICALS AND SUPPLIES FOR 10 STUDENTS:

Mossy zinc	150 g
6M Sulfuric acid	750 mL
Methyl oleate	65 mL

Practical grade may be used but the instructor should be aware that it is only about 70% methyl oleate. It would be helpful if it is possible to actually determine the purity by gas chromatographic or nmr means.

Methanol	1.5 L
10% Pd on carbon	1.2 g
Celite (Filter Aid)	

Other supplies needed (per student) are:

No. 2 one-hole rubber stopper

No. 3 one-hole rubber stopper

6 in. length rubber tubing } relatively new, with

12 in. length rubber tubing } no gas leakage

Short (7 in.) disposable pipet

UNSATURATION TEST:

   5% Bromine in CH_2Cl_2 100 mL

   (5 mL Br_2:95 mL CH_2Cl_2)

See Experiment 56 for a discussion of this reagent. It should be freshly prepared every 2-3 days.

   Methylene chloride   1 pt.

There have been several reports of fires in this experiment. No consistent pattern has been discovered, but it might be that a particularly active batch of Pd/C starts a fire during the filtration step when it is in contact with air, methanol, and hydrogen.

ANSWERS TO QUESTIONS:

1.

$$CH_2-O-\overset{\overset{\displaystyle O}{\|}}{C}-(CH_2)_7-CH=CH-(CH_2)_7CH_3$$
$$|$$
$$CH\ -O-\overset{\overset{\displaystyle O}{\|}}{C}-(CH_2)_6-(CH_2-CH=CH)_2-(CH_2)_4CH_3$$
$$|$$
$$CH_2-O-\overset{\overset{\displaystyle O}{\|}}{C}-(CH_2)_{16}CH_3\ +\ \ 3H_2$$

$$\downarrow$$

$$CH_2-O-\overset{\overset{\displaystyle O}{\|}}{C}-(CH_2)_{16}CH_3$$
$$|$$
$$CH\ -O-\overset{\overset{\displaystyle O}{\|}}{C}-(CH_2)_{16}CH_3$$
$$|$$
$$CH_2-O-\overset{\overset{\displaystyle O}{\|}}{C}-(CH_2)_{16}CH_3$$

2.   First calculate the number of moles of hydrogen absorbed. Then 1.50 g of the sample represents this same number of moles if the compound has only one double bond.

   $PV = nRT$

   or

38

$$n = \frac{PV}{RT} = \frac{(1 \text{ atm})(0.25 \text{ L})}{(0.082 \frac{\text{L-atm}}{\text{mol-}^\circ K}}(298^\circ K)} \qquad 0.01 \text{ moles } H_2 = \text{moles sample}$$

$$\text{Molecular weight} = \frac{1.50 \text{ grams}}{0.01 \text{ moles}} = 150 \text{ grams/mole}$$

3.   The formula C_5H_6 indicates 3 units of unsaturation when it is compared to C_5H_{12} (C_nH_{2n+2}). Since it only absorbs two moles of hydrogen, one of those must be a ring. Possible structures include:

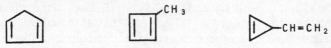

assuming the cyclopropane ring would not be reduced under these conditions of hydrogenation.

4.   The formula C_6H_{10} indicates 2 units of unsaturation when it is compared to C_6H_{14} (C_nH_{2n+2}). Since only one mole of hydrogen is absorbed, one of these units must be a ring. Possible structures include:

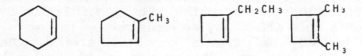

and so on.

Experiment 14

PREPARATION OF SOAP

TIME ESTIMATE: 1/3 to 1/2 period

This experiment is short and can be scheduled easily with another experiment.

CHEMICALS PER 10 STUDENTS:

Lard or other fat or oil   125 g

Sodium hydroxide   30 g

39

95% Ethanol	750 mL
Sodium chloride	625 g

ANSWERS TO QUESTIONS:

1.   Potassium salts are generally more soluble in water than sodium salts. Thus, the potassium salts of carboxylic acids are more soluble and "softer" as a result.

2.   Coconut oil yields a soap which contains a considerable amount of the salt of lauric acid (C_{12}). Since this salt has a rather low molecular weight, it is relatively soluble in water. In contrast, tallow and lard yield higher molecular weight (C_{16} and C_{18}) soaps, which are less soluble in water.

3.   Soap is soluble in water to some extent, but it is not infinitely soluble. When a common ion (Na^+) is added in the form of sodium chloride, the sodium salt of the carboxylic acid (soap) precipitates in order to establish a lower concentration of the carboxylate anion in solution.

Another explanation is that the addition of sodium chloride increases the ionic strength of the solution and "salts out" the soap. This salt effect may be explained as follows: The soap molecules (RCO_2^- Na^+) have a nonpolar R group attached to the polar carboxylate anion. The soap is soluble initially because the polar end is attracted to polar water molecules. But when the polarity of the solution is increased sharply by added salt (ions), the result is a decrease in solubility of the soap molecules. This reduced solubility results because of the greatly increased repulsion of the polar ionic solution with the nonpolar R group.

4.   In pure water, the sodium hydroxide would be soluble but the lard would not be soluble. This would result in the formation of two phases and a greatly reduced rate of reaction. Both lard and sodium hydroxide will dissolve in a mixture of ethanol and water. As a result, the rate of reaction will be increased greatly.

5.   The alkyl portions of these carboxylate ions are too small (two and three carbons, respectively) to be effective at forming micelles. The ions are small enough to be surrounded by a shell of waters of solvation, tail and all included.

Also, the hydrocarbon tails are not long enough to be effective solvents for grease molecules.

Experiment 15

PREPARATION OF A DETERGENT

TIME ESTIMATE: 1 period

This experiment may be co-scheduled with Experiment 14.

CHEMICALS PER 10 STUDENTS:

Glacial acetic acid	120 g

Chlorosulfonic acid
    Place the acid in a large buret in a hood.
    A pair of rubber gloves should be placed
    in the hood for use by the students.
	80 g
	(45 mL)

Lauryl alcohol (1-dodecanol)
    The lauryl alcohol is usually supplied in a
    narrow mouth bottle. Melt the alcohol (mp 24
    to 27°) and pour the liquid into a wide mouth
    bottle. When it crystallizes, it is easily
    broken into small pieces with a spatula.
	125 g

1-Butanol	625 mL
Sodium carbonate	125 g
Sodium phosphate ($Na_3PO_4 \cdot 12\ H_2O$)	15 g

Saturated sodium carbonate solution
    Dissolve 600 g of $Na_2CO_3 \cdot 10\ H_2O$ in 1
    liter of water.
	250 mL

Soap solution (not needed if Exp. 14 is
    performed)
    Add one bar of Ivory soap to 1 liter of
    distilled water. Stir the solution oc-
    casionally and allow the mixture to stand
    overnight. Remove the remainder of the bar.
    The mixture can be used directly.
	125 mL

4% Calcium chloride solution   10 mL
    Dissolve 4 g of calcium chloride in 100
    mL of water.

SPECIAL EQUIPMENT:

    Oven adjusted to 80°

    Hot plates

_____

ANSWERS TO QUESTIONS:

1.

$$R\ddot{O}H \ + \ Cl\overset{\overset{O}{\|}}{\underset{\underset{O}{\|}}{-S}}-OH \ \underset{slow}{\longrightarrow} \ R-O-\overset{H \ \ O}{\underset{\underset{Cl}{} \ \ O}{S}} \ \longrightarrow \ R-\overset{H \ \ O}{\underset{O \ + \ Cl^-}{O-S}}-OH \ \overset{-H^+}{\longrightarrow}$$

$$R\ddot{O}-\overset{O}{\underset{O}{S}}-OH$$

2.   Sodium carbonate is basic enough to neutralize the lauryl
ester of sulfuric acid ($ROSO_3H$) but not basic enough to hydrolyze the ester bond in the product. Other bases such as sodium hydroxide could hydrolyze the ester bond to give lauryl
alcohol and sulfate ion.

3.   A cationic detergent would also form micelles except, un-
like with anionic detergents, the outer surface of the micelle
would consist of positively charged "heads" (+ ~~~~~).

4.   See answer to questions 5, Experiment 14 (soap).

5. $CH_3(CH_2)_{10}CH_2OH \ + \ H_2SO_4 \ \longrightarrow \ CH_3(CH_2)_{10}CH_2OSO_3H \ + \ H_2O$

$CH_3(CH_2)_{10}CH_2OSO_3H \ + \ Na_2CO_3 \ \longrightarrow \ CH_3(CH_2)_{10}CH_2OSO_3^-Na^+$

                                                          $+ \ NaHCO_3$

6. $\bigcirc \ + \ CH_3(CH_2)_{10}CH_2OH \ \xrightarrow[\Delta]{conc. \ H_2SO_4} \ CH_3(CH_2)_9 \overset{CH}{\underset{CH_3}{|}}\!\!-\!\!\bigcirc$

42

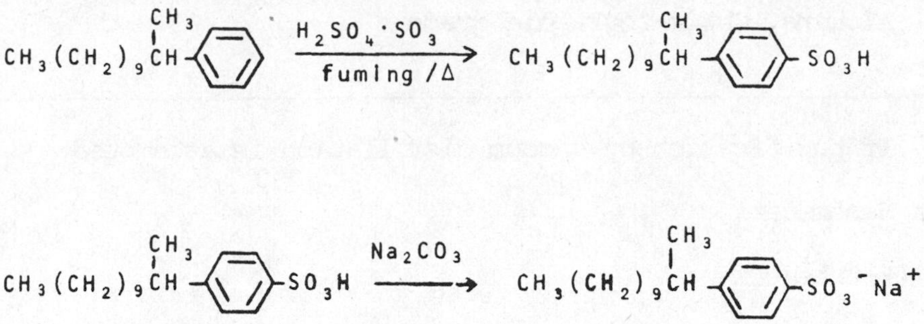

$CH_3(CH_2)_9 \overset{CH_3}{\underset{|}{CH}}$—⟨benzene⟩ $\xrightarrow[\text{fuming } / \Delta]{H_2SO_4 \cdot SO_3}$ $CH_3(CH_2)_9 \overset{CH_3}{\underset{|}{CH}}$—⟨benzene⟩—$SO_3H$

$CH_3(CH_2)_9 \overset{CH_3}{\underset{|}{CH}}$—⟨benzene⟩—$SO_3H$ $\xrightarrow{Na_2CO_3}$ $CH_3(CH_2)_9 \overset{CH_3}{\underset{|}{CH}}$—⟨benzene⟩—$SO_3^- Na^+$

Experiment 16

N,N-DIETHYL-m-TOLUAMIDE:

THE INSECT REPELLENT "OFF"

TIME ESTIMATE: 1-2 periods

CHEMICALS AND SUPPLIES PER 10 STUDENTS:

3-Methylbenzoic acid (m-toluic acid)	50 g
Thionyl chloride	55 mL (90 g)
Diethylamine	125 mL (90 g)
5% Aqueous sodium hydroxide solution	500 mL
10% Aqueous hydrochloric acid solution	250 mL
Anhydrous ether	1 L
Anhydrous sodium sulfate	30 g

If purification by chromatography is attempted:
Chromatographic columns, 25 mm x 200 mm   5-10
   Make these columns from 25 mm tubing.
   Attach a 25 mm x 200 mm test tube to
   the top and 6 mm glass tubing to the
   bottom.

Petroleum ether   1 L

If purification by vacuum distillation is attempted:

Manometers

Y-tubes

SPECIAL NOTES:

The chromatographic method seems to work best. Apparently some decomposition takes place in the distillation process.

ANSWERS TO QUESTIONS:

1.

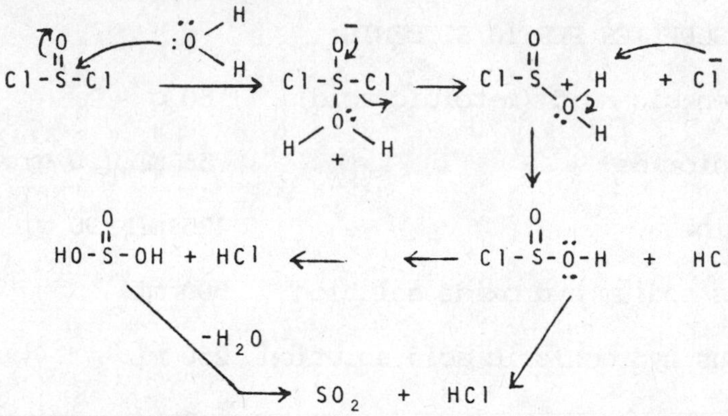

$$HO-S-OH + HCl \longleftarrow \longleftarrow Cl-S-\ddot{O}-H + HCl$$

$$\xrightarrow{-H_2O} SO_2 + HCl$$

2. If the acid chloride of m-toluic acid were added to water, it would be converted to the parent acid:

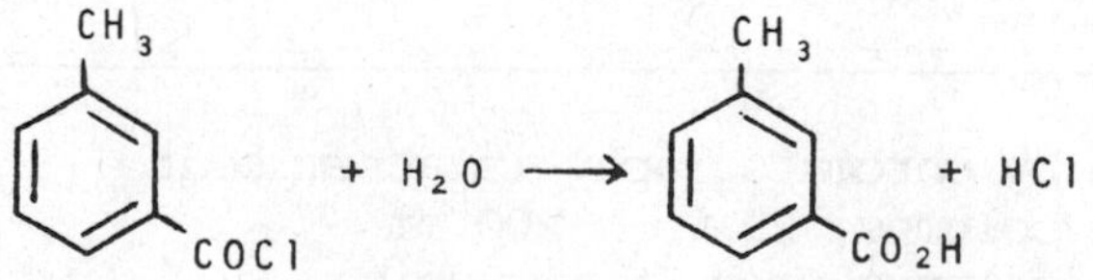

3. The white cloud which forms is due to the formation of diethylamine hydrochloride:

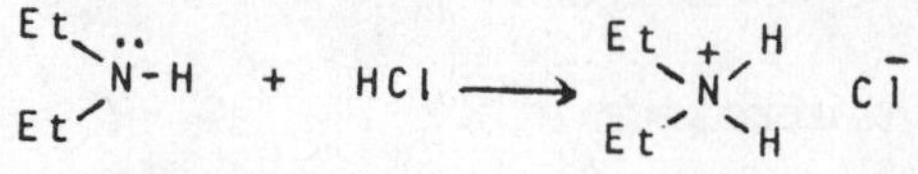

44

4. The mixture is extracted with base to remove any unreacted m-toluic acid, as well as HCl:

$$HCl + NaOH \longrightarrow NaCl + H_2O$$

5. Using the nomograph in Technique 6, Section 6.1, one would obtain 290° as the boiling point at 760 mm.

6.

7.
CH stretch	2800–3100 cm^{-1}	
C=O	1640 cm^{-1}	
C=C aromatic	1400–1600 cm^{-1}	

Experiment 17

GAS CHROMATOGRAPHIC ANALYSIS OF GASOLINES

TIME ESTIMATE: Less than 1/2 period
This experiment requires very little in-class time, and it may be co-scheduled with another experiment.

CHEMICALS PER 10 STUDENTS:

Pentane   5 mL

Hexane	5 mL
Cyclohexane	5 mL
Heptane	5 mL
Toluene	5 mL
m-Xylene	5 mL
Ethanol	5 mL
Gasoline (if provided by the instructor) }	10 mL of one type or 5 mL of each brand or grade

OTHER EQUIPMENT REQUIRED:

Gas chromatograph
    See note on page 135 of text for the preparation of this instrument.

Hypodermic syringe (10 microliter or smaller)

Sample vials or metal containers 10 (if students are to collect gasoline samples.

ANSWERS TO QUESTIONS:

1.   Regular gasolines should show relatively small amounts of toluene and xylenes. The premium gasolines should show increased amounts of these aromatic hydrocarbons, since they are added to increase the octane rating of gasoline.

2.   Benzene has a higher vapor pressure than toluene; toluene has a higher vapor pressure than m-xylene. Gas chromatographic separations depend not only on polarity but also on volatility. The more volatile components have shorter retention times, provided that their polarities are smaller. Such is the case with these aromatic hydrocarbons.

3.   An unleaded gasoline would be expected to show relatively large amounts of toluene and xylenes. Since tetraethyl lead is not used to raise the octane rating, the aromatic hydrocarbons are used for that purpose.

4.   Tetraethyl lead is present in such small quantities in gasoline that it would not be detected in this experiment.

Also, its boiling point is quite high.

5. The composition of a given grade of gasoline may vary
slightly from one brand to another. These differences may be
difficult to detect, however, and a great deal of experience
would be required to make a precise identification.

Experiment 18

ESSENTIAL OILS FROM SPICES

TIME ESTIMATE: 1 period, with some additional time required
    to obtain spectra.

CHEMICALS PER 10 STUDENTS:

Spices
  Choices include ground cloves,
  allspice, ground cumin, and
  ground cinnamon (available from
  grocery store or wholesaler)
	175 g total

Methylene chloride	250 mL
Sodium sulfate (anhydrous)	50 g
Sodium hydroxide solution (1M) 40 g/L liter of solution	250 mL
Benzoyl chloride	10 mL
Semicarbazide hydrochloride	10 g
Sodium acetate (anhydrous)	10 g
Ethanol (absolute)	50 mL
Methanol	100 mL

SPECIAL NOTE:

Some of the derivatives may be hard to prepare and puri-
fy. It might be more useful for the students to determine infrared spectra, rather than to prepare derivatives.

ANSWERS TO QUESTIONS:

1. The boiling points of these substances are rather high, and distillation at high temperature would increase the risk that they would decompose. Furthermore, simple distillation in the presence of other materials present after the extractions increases the risk of decomposition.

2. a) $P°_{substance}$ = 760-733 = 27 mm at 99°C

$$\frac{\text{moles substance}}{\text{moles water}} = \frac{P°_{substance}}{P°_{water}} = \frac{27}{733} = 0.037$$

$1 \text{ g water} = \frac{1}{18} = 0.056 \text{ moles}$

moles substance = (0.037)(0.056) = 0.0021

g substance = (moles)(M.W) = (0.0021)(150)

= 0.31 grams

b) (0.10)(100) = 10 g of substance

$\frac{10}{X} = \frac{0.31}{1}$;   0.31 X = 10

X = 32.3 g of water

3. The assumption that the substance is totally insoluble in water may not be strictly correct. In most cases the substance has some solubility in water. The amount of water which is required to steam distill the substance totally then becomes the amount calculated plus an additional amount required to distill the substance dissolved in water. Often one continues the steam distillation for several minutes after the distillate has become clear, in order to ensure that the distillation is complete.

Experiment 19

THIN-LAYER CHROMATOGRAPHY FOR MONITORING
THE OXIDATION OF BORNEOL TO CAMPHOR

TIME ESTIMATE: 1 period

48

This experiment may be co-scheduled with another experiment to be accomplished while the student is waiting for an extended period of reflux.

CHEMICALS AND SUPPLIES PER 10 STUDENTS:

Silica Gel G slurry
   Use methylene chloride-methanol (2:1) as
   the solvent in preparing the slurry. Use
   a 4-oz, wide-mouth, screw-cap jar.
	1 jar

Solution A
   2 g borneol dissolved in 100 mL diethyl
   ether
	100 mL

Solution B
   10 g of chromium trioxide (CrO_3) and 5 g
   of conc. sulfuric acid dissolved in 100
   mL water
	100 mL

Solution C
   2 g camphor dissolved in 100 mL diethyl
   ether
	100 mL

Methylene chloride	100 mL
Methanol	50 mL
Microscope slides	100 (clean and dry)
Wide-mouth jars (for developing tanks)	10
Iodine tanks	2
Open end capillary tubing	1 vial
Rulers with centimeter scale	2

ANSWERS TO QUESTIONS:

1.   Because of its O-H group, borneol is more polar than camphor. Owing to its greater polarity, it adheres more strongly to the adsorbent, and thus exhibits lower mobility on tlc plates than camphor.

2.   Because ether and water are immiscible, there will not be an intimate contact between borneol and chromic oxide unless the solution is shaken vigorously.

3.   To follow the esterification of benzoic acid, one would prepare a standard solution of benzoic acid and of methyl benzoate. Samples of the reaction mixture would be spotted at definite intervals, in a manner similar to Experiment 19. When the spot corresponding to benzoic acid disappeared, one would conclude that the reaction was complete. It would be expected that methyl benzoate would have a higher R_f value than benzoic acid, since methyl benzoate is much less polar than benzoic acid.

4.   The structures in Experiment 20 are the mirror images (enantiomers) of the structures shown in Experiment 19.

5.   Borneol and camphor each have a significant vapor pressure at room temperature. While left standing these substances would have evaporated from the plate by sublimation.

Experiment 20

AN OXIDATION-REDUCTION SCHEME
BORNEOL, CAMPHOR, ISOBORNEOL

TIME ESTIMATE: 2 periods (including ir spectroscopy)
        The instructor may wish to determine the nmr spectra of the borohydride reduction mixtures for only a few students and post these spectra in the laboratory rather than determining them for all of the students.

CHEMICALS PER 10 STUDENTS:

Sodium dichromate dihydrate   25 g

Conc. sulfuric acid   20 mL
    It is recommended that the oxidizing
    reagent be prepared by the laboratory
    assistant in the ratio of 2 g of di-
    chromate : 8 mL water : 1.6 mL conc.
    sulfuric acid.

Borneol (racemic)   15 g

Diethyl ether	425 mL
Anhydrous magnesium sulfate	25 g
Methanol	25 mL
Sodium borohydride	4 g

Check purity as indicated in footnote 4 on page 155 of the text.

| 5% Sodium bicarbonate solution | 125 mL |

Dissolve 50 g in 1 liter water

SPECIAL EQUIPMENT:

Light source (lamp or flashlight)
One per 10 students to allow observation of the dark
interface

Hot plate, 70 watt type is satisfactory

Sublimation apparatus
See list of supplies given in Exp. 6.

ANSWERS TO QUESTIONS:

1. Camphor:
    $C=O$ band at 1755 cm^{-1}
    C-H bands at 3000 cm^{-1}

    Borneol and Isoborneol
    O-H band (free) at 3625 cm^{-1}
    O-H band (H bonded) at 3400 cm^{-1}
    C-H bands centered at 2950 cm^{-1}

    CCl_4 solvent appears at 780 cm^{-1} in the spectra.

2. The gem-dimethyl groups are nearly magnetically equivalent in borneol and have approximately equal chemical shift
values because the electronegative oxygen atom is pointing
away from the methyl groups. However, in isoborneol, the gem-
dimethyl groups are not magnetically equivalent. One methyl
group has a different chemical shift value, and they appear as
separate peaks.

3. The camphor has not been reduced completely. This fact

is determined because of the presence of a band at 1760 cm^{-1}, a typical region for carbonyl absorption. If the reduction has been complete, this band would not have been present in the product.

4. $16\ H^+ + 2\ Cr_2O_7^{2-} + 3\ RCH_2OH \rightarrow 4\ Cr^{3+} + 3\ RCOOH + 11\ H_2O$

5. The structures given in this experiment are the mirror-images (enantiomers) of those given in Experiment 19.

6. K (camphor) = 39.7 °C/m

    m.p. (pure camphor) = 179 °C

$$\Delta T = Km$$

$$= (39.7)(0.5) = 19.9° = \text{freezing point depression}$$

    m.p. of impure camphor = 159°

7. The carbon-13 peaks are assigned as follows:

Camphor
a = 9.1 PPM q
b = 19.0 q
c = 19.6 q
d = 26.9 t
e = 29.8 t
f = 43.1 t
g = 43.1 d
h = 46.6 s
i = 57.4 s
j = 218.4 (not shown)

Borneol		Isoborneol
a = 13.2 q		11.2
b,c = 18.5 q and 20.0 q		20.1, 20.4
d,e = 25.9 t and 28.1 t		27.2, 33.9
f = 38.8 t		40.4
g = 45.0 d		45.0
h,i = 47.8 s and 49.3 s		46.2, 48.9
j = 77.0 d		79.7

Experiment 21

SPEARMINT AND CARAWAY OILS:
(−) AND (+)−CARVONES

TIME ESTIMATE: 2 periods

This experiment may be scheduled along with another experiment. One-half of the class should conduct this experiment and the other half, another experiment that does not require the use of aspirators. In this way, the water pressure will be high enough to obtain adequate pressures at the aspirator. Alternatively, or in addition, the students may work in pairs. Also, an attempt should be made to divide the class so that each half works with a different oil and the results should be compared. Each vacuum setup should have a manometer in the system.

It has been noted in the literature that caraway oil may foam somewhat in certain instances, usually at higher pressures. See: S.L. Murov and M. Pickering, J. Chem. Ed., 50 (1973). At pressures below 40 mm, foaming should not be expected. If foaming is experienced, it will usually stop once the limonene fraction (lower bp) has been removed.

CHEMICALS AND SUPPLIES:

30 mL of spearmint or caraway seed oil for each student
   or pair of students
      Spearmint oil is available from City Chemical Co.,
      New York, N.Y. Caraway oil is available from Amend
      Drug and Chemical Co., Irvington, N.J.

Glass wool (Pyrex), enough to wrap each fractionating column and distilling head

Stainless steel sponge, No. 775 King Size
   Available from Gottschalk Metal Sponge Corp.,
   Philadelphia, PA. Each sponge will pack two columns.

SPECIAL EQUIPMENT:

Manometers, one per vacuum setup
   An inexpensive model is shown in Technique 9, Figure
   9.4 A. They are constructed as shown in Figure 9.5.

53

Gas chromatograph, Carle Model 8000 or other suitable unit
Any relatively nonpolar column such as a 12-ft x 1/8 inch 30% GE SE-30 on Chromasorb W column may be used. The Column should be heated and equilibrated well in advance of the laboratory period. The oils, as obtained from the suppliers, may be analyzed directly to see if the column separates the limonene from the carvone.

Polarimeter
The Zeiss polarimeter is described in Technique 15

Refractometer

ANSWERS TO QUESTIONS:

1.   Infrared spectra:

Carvone: vinyl C-H at 3070 cm^{-1}
aliphatic C-H centered on 2900 cm^{-1}
C=O (conjugated) at 1660 cm^{-1}
C=C at 1635 cm^{-1}

Limonene: vinyl C-H at 3070 cm^{-1}
aliphatic C-H centered on 2900 cm^{-1}
C=C at 1635 cm^{-1}.

nmr spectrum of carvone:

6.8δ C-H vinyl (1 proton)
4.8δ C=CH_2 vinyl (2 protons)
2.6δ methylene and methine (5 protons)
1.9δ CH_3 (6 protons)

2.   Inject a sample of the distilled carvone into a gas chromatograph. Collect the carvone sample as it passes from the outlet and check its odor. Any trace impurity should have been removed by this procedure.

3.

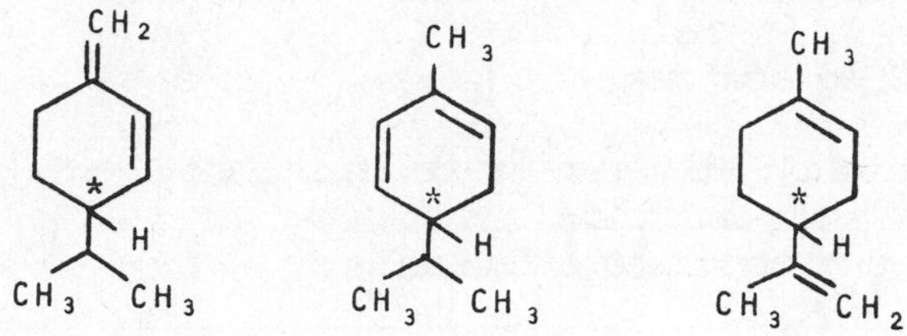

REACTIVITIES OF SOME ALKYL HALIDES

TIME ESTIMATE: 1/3 to 1/2 period
This experiment requires very little time, and it may be co-scheduled with another experiment (for example, Experiment 24).

CHEMICALS PER 10 STUDENTS:

2-Chlorobutane	10 mL
2-Bromobutane	10 mL
t-Butyl chloride (2-chloro-2-methylpropane)	10 mL
1-Chlorobutane	10 mL
Crotyl chloride (1-chloro-2-butene)	10 mL
Chloroacetone	10 mL
Benzyl chloride (α-chlorotoluene)	10 mL
Bromobenzene	10 mL
Bromocyclohexane	10 mL
Bromocyclopentane	10 mL

NOTE: It is helpful if each of the above reagents is contained in a dropper bottle. Dispensing of these chemicals is made easier thereby. Some of the materials are lachrymators. They should be stored in a hood.

55

                    15% (by weight) Sodium iodide in acetone
                                solution   250 mL
              15 g/85 g acetone

                    1% (by weight) Silver nitrate in ethanol
                                solution   250 mL
              1 g/100 g absolute ethanol

ANSWERS TO QUESTIONS:

1.   2-Bromobutane is more reactive than 2-chlorobutane because the bromo group is a better leaving group than the
chloro group. The bromo group, being larger, is held to carbon by a weaker bond than the chloro group. Bromide ion is a
more stable anion than chloride ion.

2.   Bromocyclopentane is more reactive in an S_N1 reaction
than bromocyclohexane because the starting material contains
more strain in the case of the five-membered ring. The cyclo-
pentane ring is nearly planar, and there are eclipsed confor-
mations found all around the ring. There is no such bond
eclipsing in the cyclohexane ring. When bromocyclopentane
converts to the carbonium ion, that reactive carbon changes
from tetrahedral geometry to planar, trigonal geometry. This
planar geometry removes the bond eclipsing which involved the
atoms attached to that carbon. Consequently, strain is being
relieved in the bromocyclopentane, as it is being converted to
carbonium ion. This accelerates the reactions of this molecule. Since cyclohexane compounds do not possess eclipsing
strain, they do not have this acceleration.

3.   Benzyl chloride has its reactive carbon adjacent to a
benzene ring. Electron delocalization involving this ring may
stabilize the transition state in a S_N2 reaction to some
extent, thus leading to an accelerated reaction. This acceleration is not possible in a saturated primary alkyl halide.

4.   In the sodium iodide (S_N2) test, the order of reactivity
would be:
                    3 > 2 > 4 > 1

Compound 3 contains the least steric hindrance toward backside
attack by iodide ion. The bottom side of the bicycloheptane
(the endo side) is more crowded than the upper side (the exo
side). Attack by nucleophile from the endo side would be more
difficult than attack from the exo side, so 2 would be more

56

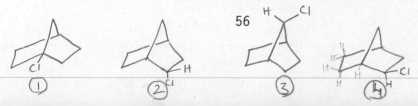

reactive than 4. Compound 1 is quite unreactive because back-side attack is not possible and because inversion cannot take place. In the silver nitrate (S_N1) test, the order of reactivity would be:

$$4 > 2 > 3 > 1$$

Compounds 4 and 2 are both accelerated with respect to compound 3 because of carbon participation in carbonium ion formation. Stereochemically, such participation is much more favorable in compound 4 than in compound 2.

The bonds around "reactive" carbon in compound 1 cannot become coplanar, so a carbonium ion cannot form and compound 1 is quite unreactive.

5.   In the sodium iodide (S_N2) test, chlorocyclopropane would be quite unreactive. The cyclopropane ring already contains a great deal of angle strain. To proceed to the S_N2 transition state would require increasing these angles further, thus increasing the angle strain. The same reasons explain the unreactive behavior which chlorocyclopropane exhibits in the silver nitrate (S_N1) test.

Experiment 23

SYNTHESIS OF n-BUTYL BROMIDE AND t-PENTYL CHLORIDE

TIME ESTIMATE: 1-2 periods for n-butyl bromide and 1 period for t-pentyl chloride

CHEMICALS PER 10 STUDENTS:

n-BUTYL BROMIDE

Sodium bromide	300 g
n-Butyl alcohol (1-butanol)	225 mL (180 g)
Conc. sulfuric acid	450 mL
Sodium hydroxide	5 g

| 10% Sodium hydroxide solution | 200 mL |
| Anhydrous calcium chloride | 20 g |

t-PENTYL CHLORIDE

t-Pentyl alcohol (t-amyl alcohol, 2-methyl-2-butanol)	275 mL	(220 g)
Conc. hydrochloric acid	625 mL	
5% Sodium bicarbonate solution	325 mL	
Anhydrous calcium chloride	20 g	

ANSWERS TO QUESTIONS (n-BUTYL BROMIDE):

1.   The sulfuric acid protonates the alcohol to produce an ionic substance which is soluble in the highly polar sulfuric acid.

$$R\ddot{O}H + H_2SO_4 \longrightarrow R\overset{..}{\underset{+}{O}}H_2 + HSO_4^-$$

2.   The sulfuric acid protonates the by-products to produce ionic substances which are soluble in the sulfuric acid.

$$R\ddot{O}R + H_2SO_4 \longrightarrow R-\overset{..}{\underset{+|}{O}}-R + HSO_4^-$$
$$\phantom{R\ddot{O}R + H_2SO_4 \longrightarrow R-}H$$

$$RCH=CH_2 + H_2SO_4 \longrightarrow R\underset{+}{C}HCH_3 + HSO_4^-$$

3.   Since the density of n-butyl chloride is 0.88 g/mL, it will appear as the upper phase at each stage of the isolation. The other phases would all be more dense.

4.   Many organic compounds will co-distill (azeotrope) with water. One may observe an incorrect boiling point in addition to obtaining an impure (cloudy) product.

ANSWERS TO QUESTIONS (t-PENTYL CHLORIDE):

1.   Since t-pentyl chloride is a tertiary alkyl halide, it can react readily with strong bases such as aqueous sodium hydroxide to form an alkene. The use of sodium bicarbonate

avoids this problem.

2.   Although some of the 2-methyl-2-butene can be produced
via the carbonium ion (E 1), most of it is likely to be produced by elimination in the presence of base (sodium bicarbonate). The 2-methyl-2-butene is removed when the distillation is performed. It has a lower boiling point than t-pentyl
chloride.

3.   The unreacted t-pentyl alcohol is removed by extraction
with water. It is soluble in water while the t-pentyl
chloride product is only slightly soluble.

4.   See the answer given above in questions 4.

Experiment 24

NUCLEOPHILIC SUBSTITUTION REACTIONS:
COMPLETING NUCLEOPHILES

TIME ESTIMATE: 1-1 1/2 Periods

CHEMICALS PER 10 STUDENTS:

Ammonium chloride	115 g
Ammonium bromide	210 g
Sulfuric acid (concentrated)	360 mL
n-Butyl alcohol (1-butanol)	60 mL
t-Butyl alcohol (2-Methyl-2-propanol)	60 mL
Saturated aqueous sodium bicarbonate	125 mL
Sodium bicarbonate (solid)	15 g
Anhydrous sodium sulfate	10 g

Crushed ice

OTHER EQUIPMENT REQUIRED:

Gas Chromatograph

Prepared as follows: column temperature, 85°;
injected port, 85°; carrier gas flow rate 50 mL/
min. The column should be a 12 foot column packed
with a rather non-polar stationary phase similar to
SE-30 silicone oil or 5% dinonyl phthalate on
Chromosorb G.

Hypodermic syringe (1 microliter)

Refractometer

SPECIAL INSTRUCTIONS:

During cold weather, it may be necessary to heat the t-
butyl alcohol on a steam bath or under hot water before the
class period in order to melt it. Also, be sure the gas
chromatograph is heated and equilibrated in advance.

It may be helpful to obtain small samples of each of the
halide products (1-chlorobutane, 1-bromobutane, 2-chloro-2-
methylpropane, and 2-bromo-2-methyl propane) to check elution
order and gas chromatographic retention times. It may also be
instructive to prepare 50/50 mixtures of the n-butyl and t-
butyl halides to ascertain whether the gas chromatographic response factor is actually unity for each and every product.
In addition, it should be noted that small amounts of 1-butene
and 2-methylpropene may occasionally be observed as a result
of competing elimination reactions.

RESULTS:

For the reaction with t-butyl alcohol, typical percentages are 50% +/- 5% for both the alkyl chloride and the alkyl
bromide. For the reaction with n-butyl alcohol, typical percentages are 85% +/- 5% for the alkyl bromide and 15% +/- 5%
for the alkyl chloride.

ANSWERS TO QUESTIONS:

1.   Bromide ion is the better nucleophile. Two explanations

are commonly given: (a) bromide ion is more "polarizable," and (b) chloride ion has a higher charge to surface area ratio (size argument) and solvates more strongly in aqueous media. As a result of this solvation, chloride ion is effectively larger and, in order to react, it must "escape" from this solvent cage. Both factors cause it to be a poor nucleophile.

2.   A mixture os S_N1 and S_N2 reactions would be expected. This would give an excess of the bromide, but not as large an excess as in the case of 1-butanol (pure S_N2).

3.   The alkenes formed by elimination are the principal by-products: 1-butene from 1-butanol, and 2-methylpropene from 2-methyl-2-propanol.

4.   The more volatile (lower bp) compound would diminish due to preferential evaporation. This would give more bromide as the chlorides have lower bp's.

5.   Unless all the solids are dissolved, one cannot be sure the reaction mixture contains a 50/50 mixture of the two nucleophiles -- an excess of one of the nucleophiles would give a larger than expected yield of the product resulting from that nucleophile.

6.   In the primary alkyl halides an <u>inductive effect</u> determines the chemical shift; the halogen is attached to the same carbon as the deshielded protons in question (X---CH_2R). Since chlorine is more electronegative than bromine, these protons are deshielded to a larger extent in the alkyl chloride than in the alkyl bromide. In the tertiary halides, on the other hand, it is a <u>field effect</u> which is more important. Bromine is larger than chlorine, and its electromagnetic influence extends further in space. The inductive effect is not as important here since Br and Cl are not connected to the same carbon as the protons in question.

7.   This is just the usual S_N1 mechanism, wherein the carbocation reacts equally with both nucleophiles present.

61

8.   In the S_N2 reaction (1-butanol), more alkyl chloride than alkyl bromide would have been the result, just the opposite of the result in water. In aprotic solvents, chloride is a better nucleophile (less solvated) than bromide.

9.   The elution order is according to boiling point. The lowest boiling point compound elutes first.

10. Yes, it is reasonable because the density of a liquid changes with temperature. A change in density should certainly affect the speed of light in a medium, and hence its refraction index.

11. It is a mole percentage.

Experiment 25

THE HYDROLYSIS OF SOME ALKYL CHLORIDES

TIME ESTIMATE: 2 periods
                 It is necessary for students to work in pairs
                 in this experiment.

CHEMICALS PER 10 STUDENTS:

t-Butyl alcohol (2-methyl-2-propanol)	75 mL
α-Phenylethyl alcohol (α-Methylbenzyl alcohol or sec-Phenethyl alcohol)	75 mL
Hydrochloric acid (concentrated)	300 mL
5% (by weight) Aqueous sodium bicarbonate	75 mL
Calcium chloride (anhydrous)	50 g
Acetone (reagent-grade, dry)	1 L
Ethanol (absolute)	1 L
Bromthymol blue indicator	10 mL
0.01 N Sodium hydroxide 0.40 g/1 liter solution	2 L

OTHER MATERIALS REQUIRED:

Magnetic stirring bars	5
50 mL Burets	5
Stopwatches or timers	5
1 mL Pipets	5

ANSWERS TO QUESTIONS:

1.   The rate constant for the data given in the tables is
$5.73 \times 10^{-2} min^{-1}$. The half life is 12.1 min.

2.   There are two principal by-products in this reaction, the
alkene and the ethyl ether for those reactions carried out in
ethanol solvent mixtures. In the hydrolysis to t-butyl
chloride, 2-methylpropene is a by-product. For those reactions run in aqueous ethanol, ethyl t-butyl ether may be
formed as well. In the hydrolysis of α-phenylethyl chloride,
styrene and ethyl α-phenylethyl ether are formed.

3.   The energy diagram for an $S_N 1$ reaction conducted in a
more aqueous solvent involves a lower energy of activation
than a similar reaction run in a less aqueous solvent. Consequently, the reaction in the more aqueous solvent is faster.
The ability of water to solvate the carbonium ion-like transition state stabilizes it. The transition state is formed more
easily, and the reaction proceeds more rapidly.

4.   It would be expected that t-cumyl chloride would react
faster than α-phenylethyl chloride in a given solvent. t-
cumyl chloride would form a tertiary carbonium ion, while α-
phenylethyl chloride would form a secondary cation. Since the
tertiary ion is more stable than a secondary ion, it should be
formed faster. Both cations involve benzyl-type resonance.

Experiment 26

CHROMIC ACID OXIDATION OF ALCOHOLS

TIME ESTIMATE: 1 period
        The actual time required to obtain the data is relatively
        short, if one does not count the waiting period for the

infinity reading. Consequently, it is possible to co-schedule this experiment with another experiment. Our method is to have the equipment available for several weeks and have the students do their kinetic runs whenever they find it convenient during that period.

CHEMICALS AND SUPPLIES PER 10 STUDENTS:

Alcohol samples Provide a choice of ethanol, 1-propanol, 2-propanol, 2-methoxyethanol, 2-chloroethanol, ethylene glycol, or 1-phenyl-ethanol.	1 mL of each alcohol
3.9 M Sulfuric acid solution This solution should be prepared by the laboratory assistant for use by the entire class. This solution does not need to be standardized, but enough should be prepared to last the entire experiment.	150 mL (double this amount if duplicate runs are required)
0.0196 M Potassium dichromate soln. This solution should be carefully prepared using distilled water. The solution does not need to be standardized, but enough must be prepared by the laboratory assistant to last for the entire experiment.	15 mL (double this amount if duplicate runs are required)

EQUIPMENT REQUIRED:

Ultraviolet-visible spectrophotometer The experiment instructions are written for a typical ultraviolet-visible instrument. Specific instructions for the particular instrument available in the laboratory must be provided by the instructor. We have found that the experiment can be completed faster if more than one instrument is available.	1 or more
Spectrophotometer cells	at least 2

64

Again, the more of these that are available, the faster the class can complete the
experiment.

50 microliter Syringe	1 per instrument
Timer (calibrated in minutes)	1 per instrument
1 mL Pipet	1 per instrument
10 mL Pipet	1 per instrument
Pipet bulb	1 per instrument

TYPICAL EXPERIMENT RESULTS:
    The following table lists the half-lives reported for
different alcohol substrates under typical experimental conditions. Because of uncontrolled experimental variables, such
as temperature variations, age of reagents, and accidental
contamination of reagents, we have observed that data obtained
in large classes shows a good deal of experimental scatter.

Alcohol	Half-life (min.)
Ethanol	10.5
1-Propanol	11.1
2-Propanol	20.6
2-Methoxyethanol	110.3
2-Chloroethanol	222.9
Ethylene glycol	36.8
1-Phenylethanol	60.2

ANSWERS TO QUESTIONS:

1. From the graph we obtain,

    slope = 0.093 min^{-1}

    k = (0.093)(2.303) = 0.213 min^{-1}

    half-life = 3.25 min.

2. The relative rates should be:

    1-propanol > ethanol > 2-methoxyethanol

65

The mechanism involves a rate-determining step where the alcohol releases its electrons to chromium while at the same time undergoing loss of a hydride species. An electron-attracting substituent, such as methoxy, would inhibit such a loss of electrons; an electron-releasing substituent such as methyl would have the opposite effect.

3. 1-Propanol reacts faster than 2-propanol. Consistent with the answer to question #2, one would expect an accelerated reaction with 2-propanol. However, 1-propanol has two hydrogens which can be lost in the oxidation, while 2-propanol has only one hydrogen. This statistical effect is more important than the substituent effect, so one sees a faster reaction with 1-propanol.

4. a) $3\ HOCH_2CH_2OH\ +\ 2\ K_2Cr_2O_7\ +\ 16\ H^+\ \longrightarrow$

$$3\ H\text{-}\overset{\overset{O}{\|}}{C}\text{-}\overset{\overset{O}{\|}}{C}\text{-}H\ +\ 4\ Cr^{3+}\ +\ 4\ K^+\ +\ 14\ H_2O$$

b)

$+\ 2\ KMnO_4\ \longrightarrow$

$+\ 2\ MnO_2\ +\ 2\ K^+\ +\ OH^-\ +\ H_2O$

c) $HO(CH_2)_4OH\ +\ K_2Cr_2O_7\ +\ 8\ H^+\ \longrightarrow$

$$HO\text{-}\overset{\overset{O}{\|}}{C}\text{-}(CH_2)_2\text{-}\overset{\overset{O}{\|}}{C}\text{-}H\ +\ 2\ Cr^{3+}\ +\ 2\ K^+\ +\ 6\ H_2O$$

d) $3\ CH_3CH_2CH_2CH=CH_2\ +\ 10\ KMnO_4\ \longrightarrow$

$$3\ CH_3CH_2CH_2\text{-}\overset{\overset{O}{\|}}{C}\text{-}O^-\ +\ 3\ CO_2\ +\ 10\ MnO_2$$

$$+\ 10\ K^+\ +\ 7\ OH^-\ +\ H_2O$$

e) $CH_3\ +\ 2\ KMnO_4\ \longrightarrow\ CH_3\text{-}\overset{\overset{O}{\|}}{C}\text{-}(CH_2)_4\text{-}\overset{\overset{O}{\|}}{C}\text{-}O^-\ +\ 2\ MnO_2$

$$+\ 2K^+\ +\ OH^-$$

Experiment 27

CYCLOHEXENE

TIME ESTIMATE: 1 period

CHEMICALS AND SUPPLIES PER 10 STUDENTS:

Cyclochexanol	220 mL (210 g)
85% Phosphoric acid (14.7 M)	60 mL (100 g)
10% Aqueous sodium carbonate (100 g/liter)	1 L
Anhydrous calcium chloride	35 g
Sodium chloride (table salt)	
For the unsaturation tests:	
Br_2/CH_2Cl_2 test solution (2% bromine by volume)	50 mL
Aqueous $KMnO_4$ solution (1% weight/volume)	50 mL
1,2-Dimethoxyethane	small bottle

ANSWERS TO QUESTIONS:

1.

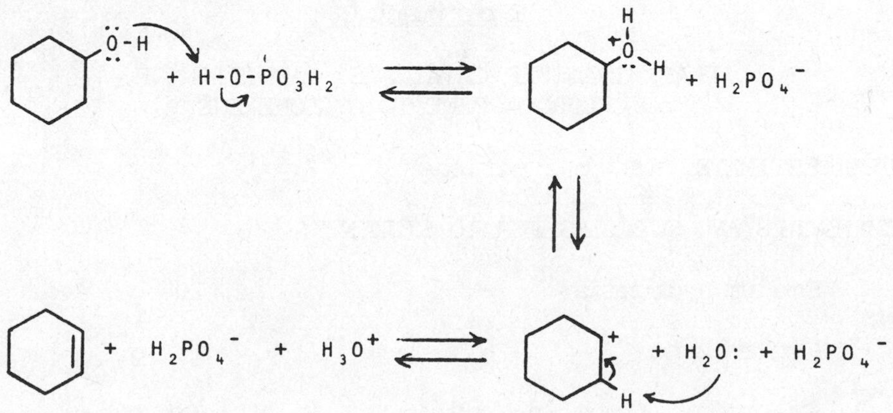

2. a) 1-methylcyclohexene   d) 1,2-dimethylcyclohexene

   b) 1-methylcyclohexene   e) cyclohexanone

   c) 4-methylcyclohexene

3. Salt is added to force a better separation of the organic layer from the water. Cyclohexanol is partially soluble in water.

4. To neutralize the excess phosphoric acid:

$$2 H_3PO_4 + 3 Na_2CO_3 \longrightarrow 2 Na_3PO_4 + 3 [H_2CO_3]$$

$$\downarrow$$

$$3 H_2O + 3 CO_2$$

5. <u>Cyclohexene</u>   <u>Cyclohexanol</u>

   CH vinyl 3040 cm^{-1} No CH vinyl   ($>3000 \text{ cm}^{-1}$)

   CH ring   2850 &   CH ring   2850 &

    methylenes 2950 cm^{-1} methylenes 2950 cm^{-1}

   C=C 1660 cm^{-1} (weak)   No C=C

   No OH   OH   3100–3600 (broad)

   ring CH_2 groups 1450   ring CH_2 groups 1450 cm^{-1}

Experiment 28

PHASE-TRANSFER CATALYSIS: ADDITION OF DICHLOROCARBENE TO CYCLOHEXENE

TIME ESTIMATE: 1 to 2 periods

CHEMICALS AND SUPPLIES PER 10 STUDENTS:

   Sodium hydroxide   200 g

   Cyclohexene   100 g

   Chloroform (keep in hood)   325 mL

Benzyltriethylammonium Chloride   13 g
     See the note to the instructor
     on page 209 of the text (foot-
     note 1) for a supplier of the
     catalyst.

Methylene chloride   650 mL

Saturated aqueous NaCl solution   375 mL
     31.7 g/100 mL water (stored
     in polyethylene bottle)

Anhydrous sodium sulfate   25 g

SPECIAL EQUIPMENT (Optional):

     Magnetic Stirrers

ANSWERS TO QUESTIONS:

1.   The reaction medium consists of two phases. Vigorous
swirling ensures that the reaction will proceed at a reasonable rate.

2.   A certain amount of water is held in the organic phase
because of the phase transfer agent (detergent effect). Saturated salt solution helps to "dry" the organic phase by
allowing water to pass into the salt solution to help dilute
it. This process is similar to that observed in osmosis, except no membrane is used.

3.   The presence or absence of unsaturation can be determined
with the bromine/CCl_4 or $KMnO_4$ tests.

4.   The chlorine atoms are located on the cyclopropane ring.
They cannot be displaced by an S_N2 reaction using iodide ion
(see answer to Question 5, Experiment 22).

5.   The C-H stretch appears at 3025 cm^{-1}.

6.   The chloroform is decomposed with base by Equations 4 and
5 on pages 205 & 206 as a competing reaction to carbene addition. Excess chloroform is needed to ensure that the product
is produced in high yield.

7. The product is contaminated with cyclohexene.

8.

$$CH_3\text{C}=C\text{CH}_3 + :CCl_2 \longrightarrow$$ (cyclopropane product with CH$_3$, H groups and CCl$_2$ ring)

$$CH_3\text{C}=C\text{H} + :CCl_2 \longrightarrow$$ (cyclopropane product with CH$_3$, H and CH$_3$ groups and CCl$_2$ ring)

9.

$$CH_2 = C\begin{smallmatrix}CH_3\\CO_2CH_3\end{smallmatrix} \xrightarrow{:CCl_2}$$ (cyclopropane product with CH$_3$, CO$_2$CH$_3$ groups and CCl$_2$ ring)

$$\xrightarrow{CHCl_3} Cl_3C-CH_2-\overset{CH_3}{\underset{|}{C}H}-CO_2CH_3$$

10. a) (norbornene + :CCl$_2$ → cyclopropane adduct with CCl$_2$, –Cl$^-$ →; cation + Cl$^-$ → dichloride product)

b) (cyclopentadiene + :CCl$_2$ → bicyclic adduct with CCl$_2$; via –Cl$^-$ and –H$^+$ to chlorobenzene; via :CCl$_2$ to tetrachloro adduct)

Experiments 29A and 29B

MARKOVNIKOV AND ANTI-MARKOVNIKOV HYDRATION OF STYRENE
29A HYDROBORATION-OXIDATION OF STYRENE
29B OXYMERCURATION OF STYRENE

TIME ESTIMATE: 2 periods for either experiment.
We usually have the students pair up so that one student
does the hydroboration experiment while the other does
the oxymercuration experiment. Students compare their
results when they submit their laboratory reports.

CHEMICALS AND SUPPLIES PER 10 STUDENTS:

EXPERIMENT 29A   (Hydroboration-oxidation)

Calcium chloride	125 g
Styrene (in hood)	25 g

Borane-tetrahydrofuran complex
    (1.0 M solution in tetrahydrofuran)
    Available from Aldrich Chemical Co.
	70 mL

30% Hydrogen peroxide	25 mL
3 M Sodium hydroxide solution	50 mL
Diethyl ether	500 mL
Saturated sodium bicarbonate	250 mL
Anhydrous magnesium sulfate	15 g

SUPPLIES AND EQUIPMENT:

Wooden applicator sticks	10
10 mL Disposable hypodermic syringes (with needles)	1 per student
Rubber septa to fit a ST 19/22 joint (or other appropriate size)	1 per student

Experiment 29B (Oxymercuration)

Mercuric acetate	100 g
Styrene	35 g
Diethyl ether	700 mL
6 M Sodium hydroxide	160 mL

3 M Sodium hydroxide	325 mL

Fresh sodium borohydride   7 g
>NOTE: Fresh sodium borohydride must be used. It should also be finely powdered. Place a small amount of powdered material in some methanol. It should bubble vigorously if the hydride is active.

Anhydrous magnesium sulfate	15 g

SUPPLIES AND EQUIPMENT:

Magnetic stirrers	1 per student
Magnetic stirring bars	1 per student
Waste container for mercury	1 per class, in a hood

SPECIAL EQUIPMENT:

Gas chromatography, see Experiment 21 for a suitable instrument and column. Prepare the chromatograph according to the instructions given in footnote 2, page 219 of the textbook.

RESULTS:

In some cases, students may have a considerable amount of unreacted styrene in their samples. This does not change the results, however, since the relative amounts of the alcohols can be determined by gas chromatography.

Hydroboration-oxidation: about 82% 2-phenylethanol (anti-Markovnikov addition); about 18% 1-phenylethanol (Markovnikov addition). Regioselective.

Oxymercuration: 100% 1-phenylethanol (Markovnikov addition). Regiospecific.

ANSWERS TO QUESTIONS:

1. SEE RESULTS SECTION ABOVE.

2. HYDROBORATION-OXIDATION

a)

b)

$$Ph \overset{CH_3}{\underset{H}{\text{—}}} C \overset{CH_3}{\underset{OH}{\text{—}}} H \ + \ Ph\text{-}\overset{CH_3}{\underset{OH}{C}}CH_2CH_3$$

c)

$$Ph \overset{CH_3}{\underset{H}{\text{—}}} C \text{—} \overset{H}{\underset{OH}{C}} CH_3 \ + \ Ph\text{-}\overset{CH_3}{\underset{OH}{C}}\text{-}CH_2CH_3$$

d)

OXYMERCURATION

a)

b)

$$Ph\text{-}\overset{CH_3}{\underset{OH}{C}}CH_2CH_3$$

c)

$$Ph\text{-}\overset{CH_3}{\underset{OH}{C}}CH_2CH_3$$

d)

Experiment 30A and 30B

30A TRIPHENYLMETHANOL
30B BENZOIC ACID

TIME ESTIMATE: 2 periods for either experiment

We find that students will not need iodine to start the reaction if they have been careful to dry the apparatus completely. In the first period, the Grignard Reagent (phenylmagnesium bromide) should be prepared and added to the substrate. In the case of triphenylmethanol (Experiment 30A) the procedure should be carried forward to the point where the addition product is dried (in ether) over anhydrous sodium sulfate (page 229, line 14). The product may be left in solution over sodium sulfate (tightly stoppered flask) until the next period. In the case of benzoic acid (Experiment 30B), the procedure may be stopped immediately after the addition of the Grignard Reagent to the Dry Ice (page 231, end of first paragraph of Procedure 30B). If this is done, ether must be added at the beginning of the second period.

CHEMICALS AND SUPPLIES PER 10 STUDENTS:

Experiment 30A   (Triphenylmethanol)

Bromobenzene	68 g (45 ml)
Magnesium turnings	11 g
Anhydrous ether	500 mL
Solvent grade ether	200 mL
Benzophenone	55 g
Anhydrous sodium sulfate	20 g
Petroleum ether (30-60°)	350 mL
Ligroin (60-90°)	650 mL
6M HCl	125 mL
Iodine	(small bottle)
Calcium chloride (drying tubes)	50 g

Experiment 30B   (Benzoic Acid)

Bromobenzene	68 g (90 mL)
Magnesium turnings	11 g
Anhydrous ether	500 mL
Solvent grade ether	375 mL
Dry ice	1/4 lb
5% Aqueous NaOH	500 mL
Conc. HCl	150 mL
Calcium chloride (drying tubes)	50 g
Iodine	(small bottle)

REACTIONS OF TRIPHENYLMETHANOL

1. Triphenylcarbonium Ion Formation

Place a small amount of purified triphenylmethanol in a small test tube and add dropwise concentrated sulfuric acid until the solid dissolves. Record the color of the solution. Pour the sulfuric acid mixture into about 10 mL of water and record the result.

2. Preparation of Bromotriphenylmethane

Dissolve 0.5 g of purified triphenylmethanol in 10 mL of glacial acetic acid in a 125 mL Erlenmeyer flask, with the aid of slight warming on a steam bath. Add 1.0 mL of 47 – 49% aqueous hydrobromic acid and heat the mixture on a steam bath. Cool the mixture in an ice bath and collect the bromotriphenyllmethane by vacuum filtration on a small Büchner funnel. Wash the solid thoroughly with 3 mL of <u>cold</u> ligroin (65-90°) so that the odor of acetic acid is removed, and dry the product quickly in an oven at 80° for 5 minutes. Weigh the bromotriphenylmethane, calculate the percentage yield, and obtain the melting point (literature m.p. 152°C). Store the product in a tightly stoppered vial.

3. Triphenylmethyl Radical Formation

(1) $2\ Ph_3CBr\ +\ :Zn\ \longrightarrow\ 2\ Ph_3C\cdot\ +\ ZnBr_2$

                         Colored

(2) $Ph_3C\cdot\ +\ \cdot CPh_3 \rightleftharpoons Ph_3C - CPh_3$

                              (I)

(3) $Ph_3C\cdot\ +$

(III) (IV) Colored   (II) Colorless

(4) $Ph_3C\cdot\ +\ O_2\ \longrightarrow\ Ph_3C-O-O\cdot\ \xrightarrow{Ph_3C\bullet}\ Ph_3C-O-O-CPh_3$

                                       (V) Colorless

The colored triphenylmethyl radical, first discovered in 1900 by Gomberg, is obtained by reduction of bromotriphenylmethane with zinc metal as shown in equation (1). For years it was thought that the dimer formed by equation (2) was hexaphenylethane (I), and that this head-to-head dimer was in equilibrium with the radical. In 1968 it was reported (see references) that the actual dimer was the head-to-tail isomer (II) formed in essence by the reaction of radical (III) with its "resonance" structure (IV) by equation (3). Therefore, the colorless dimer (II) is in equilibrium with the colored triphenylmethyl radical as given in equation (3). When oxygen is present, the radical reacts quickly with oxygen (a diradical) to give the colorless peroxide (V) as shown in equation (4). Within a short time most of the dimer (II) is converted to the peroxide IV) via the radical (III).

Procedure: Dissolve a small amount (about 0.5 cm on the end of a spatula) of the bromotriphenylmethane prepared above in about 3 mL of toluene in a test tube. Add about the same amount of zinc powder (see note below), stopper the tube and observe the color of the solution. Do not shake the tube. After one minute, quickly decant the colored solution away from the solid into another test tube. Stopper the tube and shake it vigorously for several minutes, but remove the cork periodically to admit air. Observe the changes which occur, and allow the unstoppered test tube to stand in an ice bath for 30 minutes. Record the results and comment on the structure of any product which forms.

> NOTE: If the solution is quickly degassed with nitrogen to remove oxygen following the addition of zinc and stoppered, the triphenylmethyl radical will have a much longer life-time. Peroxide formation (cloudiness) will be retarded. The instructor should check to see if the zinc metal is active.

References:

H. Lankamp, W. Th. Nauta, and C. MacLean, Tetrahedron Letters 249 (1968).

J. M. McBride, "The Hexaphenylethane Riddle," Tetrahedron, 30, 2009 (1974).

4. Triphenylmethyl Anion Formation (Demonstration by Instructor)

The preparation of the sodium amalgam and triphenylmethyl sodium is best conducted by the instructor as a demonstration. Place 34 g of mercury in a 50 mL standard tapered round bottom flask and add 0.43 g of sodium in small pieces. CAUTION: The reaction is violent. Each piece of sodium should react before the next piece is added. Cool the amalgam to room temperature and add about 30 mL of dry ether (dried over sodium wire, if possible) to the flask. Add 0.35 g of the bromotriphenyl-methane prepared above, insert the glass stopper securely into the flask, and shake <u>vigorously</u> for about 5 minutes. Since the reaction is exothermic, release the pressure periodically during that time. A color change should be observed within a few minutes. Allow the solution to stand until the sediment settles somewhat. The solution should be used as soon as possible. Observe and record the color of the carbanion. With a clean and <u>dry</u> pipet or dropper draw a sample from the flask and place it in a test tube containing some water. De-scribe what happens and give a balanced equation for the reac-tion with water. Check the pH of the aqueous layer to see if the result is consistent with the prediction from the equa-tion.

REACTIONS OF BENZOIC ACID

1.   <u>Acidity of Aqueous Solutions</u>

Place a small amount of the purified <u>benzoic acid</u> into a test tube and add about 2 mL of water. Heat the tube slightly to dissolve, or nearly dissolve, the solid. With blue litmus paper, check the acidity of the solution and record the result. Repeat the test with a sample of <u>phenol</u>.

2.   <u>Solubility Tests</u>

Into each of three test tubes add about 2 mL of 5% aqueous sodium bicarbonate. Label the tubes and place a few crystals or pieces of one of the following compounds into each test tube: benzoic acid, 2-naphthol, and 2,4-dinitrophenol. Gently tap the test tube with a finger to assure mixing. The disappearance of the solid, or the appearance of mixing lines, indicates that the substance is dissolving. If the solid dis-solves slowly, allow the mixture to stand for a while and then check it again. For the compounds that dissolve quickly, check for evolution of carbon dioxide gas. Add more solid if necessary to observe the gas. Record the solubility behavior of the three compounds. Repeat the solubility test on the three compounds using 5% aqueous sodium hydroxide, and record the results. Discuss the structural differences that give rise to the observed solubility behavior. Also comment on the <u>change</u> in color which one observes with the 2,4-dinitrophenol in basic solution.

77

3.   <u>Preparation of Ethyl Benzoate</u>

Place 0.3 g of <u>dry</u> benzoic acid (the crude material is satisfactory), 3 mL of absolute ethanol, and 10 drops of concentrated sulfuric acid into a test tube. Heat the contents of the tube in a boiling water bath for about 30 minutes (with careful heating no boiling stone is needed). During that time, the volume will decrease somewhat. Cool the contents of the test tube to room temperature, add 10 mL of diethyl ether and transfer the mixture to a separatory funnel. Add 10 mL of 5% aqueous bicarbonate, and shake the funnel vigorously, but be sure to vent the funnel <u>frequently</u> to release the pressure. When the "whoosh" is no longer audible, drain and discard the lower aqueous layer, and reextract the remaining ether layer with another 10 mL portion of 5% sodium bicarbonate. Again separate and discard the lower aqueous phase, and pour the ether layer into a small Erlenmeyer flask. Dry the ether layer with a small amount of anhydrous magnesium sulfate, gravity filter the solution to remove the drying agent, and evaporate the ether on a steam bath. Note the characteristic odor of the product. The infrared spectrum and/or the nmr spectrum of the product may be determined.

ANSWERS TO QUESTIONS:

1.   Most likely, benzene is formed by reaction of phenylmagnesium bromide with traces of water in the ether or from the air.

$$C_6H_5MgBr + H_2O \longrightarrow C_6H_6 + Mg(OH)Br$$

2.   Petroleum ether is used because the major impurity, biphenyl, is extremely soluble and will not crystallize from this solvent.

3. $C_6H_5COOH + OH^- \longrightarrow C_6H_5COO^- + H_2O$

The extraction of the ether layer with base removes the benzoic acid, extracting it into the aqueous layer as its salt. The biphenyl is left behind in the ether layer.

4.   <u>Triphenylmethanol</u>   <u>Benzoic Acid</u>

| OH | 3450 cm^{-1} (broad) | acid OH | $2400\text{--}3400 \text{ cm}^{-1}$ very broad due to dimerization (H-bonding) |

78

CH   aromatic 3050 cm^{-1} Overlaps CH region

C=C aromatic   C=O 1690 cm^{-1}

       bands 1400-1600 cm^{-1} C=C aromatic doublets
                                         1420 and 1600 cm^{-1}

C-O tertiary alcohol   C-O doublet 1300 cm^{-1}
      one of bands 950-
            1350 cm^{-1}

5.

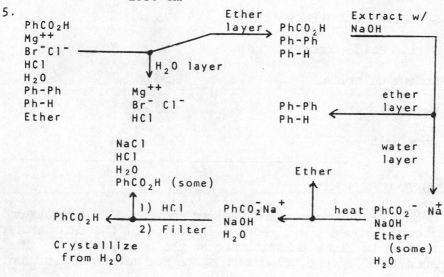

6. a) $CH_3CH_2\overset{\text{O}}{\underset{\|}{C}}H$ + CH_3CH_2MgBr $\xrightarrow{\text{2) } H_3O^+}$ $CH_3CH_2\underset{\underset{OH}{|}}{C}HCH_2CH_3$

b) $CH_3CH_2-\overset{\text{O}}{\underset{\|}{C}}-CH_2CH_3$ + CH_3MgBr $\longrightarrow$ $CH_3CH_2-\overset{\overset{CH_3}{|}}{\underset{\underset{OH}{|}}{C}}-CH_2CH_3$

   or $CH_3CH_2-\overset{\text{O}}{\underset{\|}{C}}-CH_3$ + CH_3CH_2MgBr $\longrightarrow$ $CH_3-CH_2-\overset{\overset{CH_3}{|}}{\underset{\underset{OH}{|}}{C}}-CH_2CH_3$

c) $CH_3CH_2CH_2CH_2CH_2-MgBr$ $\xrightarrow[\text{2) } H_3O^+]{\text{1) } CO_2}$ $CH_3CH_2CH_2CH_2CH_2CO_2H$

d) $Ph-\overset{\text{O}}{\underset{\|}{C}}H$ + CH_3CH_2MgBr $\longrightarrow$ $Ph-\underset{\underset{OH}{|}}{C}HCH_2CH_3$

   or $CH_3CH_2\overset{\text{O}}{\underset{\|}{C}}H$ + $PhMgBr$ $\longrightarrow$ $Ph-\underset{\underset{OH}{|}}{C}HCH_2CH_3$

NITRATION OF METHYL BENZOATE

TIME ESTIMATE: 1 period

CHEMICALS PER 10 STUDENTS:

Methyl benzoate	70 g
Sulfuric acid (concentrated)	175 mL
Nitric acid (concentrated)	50 mL
Sodium chloride	50 g
Methanol	250 mL
Rock salt	

ANSWERS TO QUESTIONS:

1.   Methyl m-nitrobenzoate is formed instead of the ortho or para isomer because the directive influence of the carbomethoxy group is to favor substitution at the meta position. The resonance forms of the transition state for meta substitution.

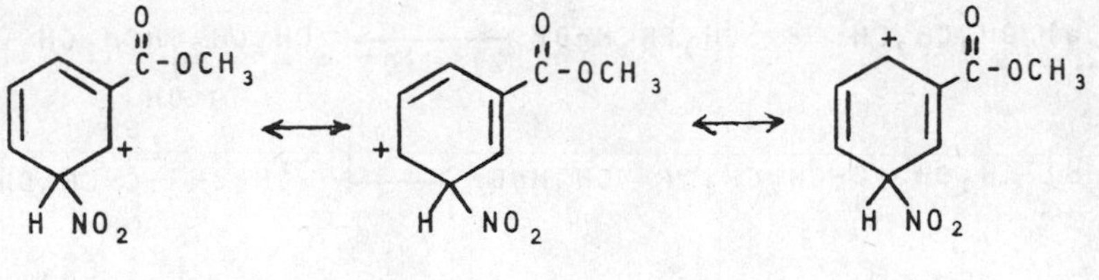

do not involve placing positive charge next to the electron-deficient carbon of the carbonyl group, as one would observe in para (or ortho) substitution.

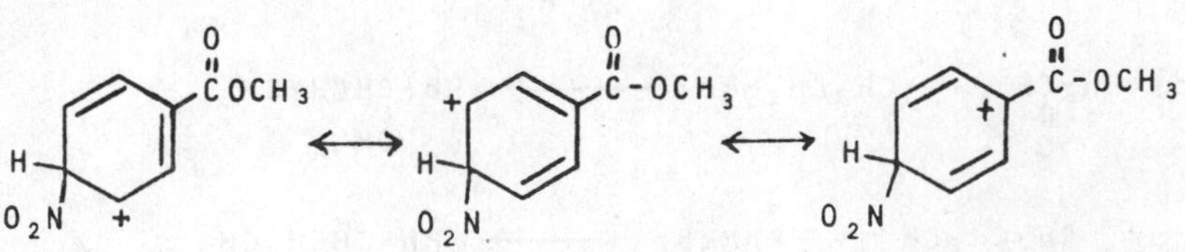

80

2.	As the reaction temperature rises, the rate at which di-
nitration of methyl benzoate increases. An elevated temperature is required for dinitration since the first nitro group,
together with the carbomethoxy group, deactivates the aromatic
ring toward further substitution.

3.	3050 cm^{-1} Aromatic C-H stretch	2800–2900 cm^{-1} Methyl
	C-H stretch and C-H
	1710 cm^{-1} C=O stretch of ester	stretch of Nujol

	1620–1450 cm^{-1} C=C stretch of aromatic ring (obscured by
	Nujol peaks)

	1440 and 1350 CH$_2$ and CH$_3$ C-H
	bending of Nujol

	NOTE: The characteristic N-O stretching peaks of the
	nitro group are obscured by the C-H bending peaks
	of Nujol.

4.	Nitration products (major products only):

	Benzene: nitrobenzene
	Toluene: o-nitrotoluene and p-nitrotoluene
	Chlorobenzene: o-chloronitrobenzene and p-chloronitro-
	benzene
	Benzoic acid: m-nitrobenzoic acid

Experiment 32

p-NITROANILINE

TIME ESTIMATE: 2 periods

CHEMICALS PER 10 STUDENTS:

Acetanilide	40 g
	This may be student-prepared material
	from Experiment 2.

Sulfuric acid (concentrated)	125 mL

Nitric acid (concentrated)	25 mL

Aqueous ammonium hydroxide (concentrated)	350 mL

81

Ethanol (95%)   1500 mL

Decolorizing carbon (Norit)   10 g

SUPPLIES REQUIRED FOR THIN LAYER CHROMATOGRAPHY:

Microscope slides   40
     (These must be carefully cleaned and
     dried if they have been used previously.)

Silica Gel G slurry   1 jar
     Use methylene chloride as the solvent
     in preparing the slurry. Use the same
     size jars as were used for developing
     tanks.

Wide-mouth jars (for use as developing tanks)   10

Iodine tanks   2

Open end capillary tubes   1 vial

Rulers with centimeter scale   2

Methylene chloride   500 mL

ANSWERS TO QUESTIONS:

1.   The acetamido group is ortho-para directing due to its
unshared pair of electrons, which it can use to stabilize the
intermediate cation (and hence the transition state). The
appropriate resonance forms are:

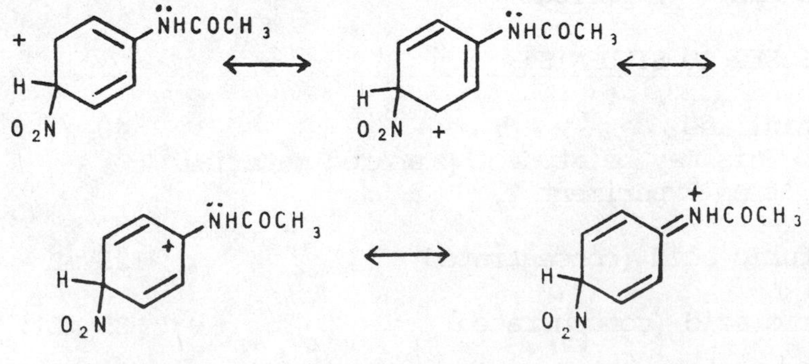

It is less strongly activating than an amino group because the electron-withdrawing nature of the acetyl group reduces the availability of the unshared electron pair for delocalization into the aromatic ring.

2.

3.   Fractional crystallization from ethanol, where the mother liquor is saved, if repeated, would yield a mother liquor which was progressively enriched in the ortho isomer. A final crystallization of this isomer would afford pure o-nitroaniline.

4.   The column would be packed with Silica Gel, using a solvent similar to methylene chloride for elution. Since o-nitrotoluene is less polar than the para isomer, it would be expected to pass through the column at a faster rate.

5.   The mononitration product is N-methyl-m-nitrobenzamide.

In the case of acetanilide, the substituent attached directly
to the aromatic ring is the -NH- group. This group directs
substitution to the ortho and para positions. In the case of
N-methylbenzamide, the substituent attached directly to the
ring is the C=O group. This group directs substitution to the
meta position.

Experiment 33

FRIEDEL-CRAFTS ACYLATION

TIME ESTIMATE: 2 periods

CHEMICALS AND SUPPLIES PER 10 STUDENTS:

Dichloromethane (methylene chloride)	1 L
Anhydrous aluminum chloride	175 g
Acetyl chloride	100 g
Hydrochloric acid, concentrated	300 mL
Saturated sodium bicarbonate solution 6.9 g/100 mL water	700 mL
Anhydrous sodium sulfate	50 g
Calcium chloride (drying tubes)	100 g
Anhydrous magnesium sulfate	15 g

The following chemicals will be needed in an amount of
approximately 10 g per student (0.075 mole). Each
student will use (or be assigned) one of the chemicals
from this list:

Toluene

o-Xylene (1,2-dimethylbenzene)

m-Xylene (1,3-dimethylbenzene)

p-Xylene (1,4-dimethylbenzene)

Ethylbenzene

84

Mesitylene (1,3,5-trimethylbenzene)

Cumene (isoproylbenzene)

Anisole (methoxybenzene)

Solvents for spectroscopy:

Carbon tetrachloride	1 pt
Deuteriochloroform	100 mL

SPECIAL EQUIPMENT:

Manometers

NMR tubes

IR salt plates

SPECIAL NOTES:

It is recommended that the anhydrous aluminum chloride be placed in a hood along with a balance (a triple beam will suffice). All weighing can then be conducted in the hood to minimize noxious vapors.

We prefer to keep the solvents for spectroscopy in a small (1 pint) bottle, with a test tube attached to the side, which in turn contains a disposable pipet for dispensing the small quantities required. This bottle is stored in a hood where an area is set aside for preparation of spectroscopic samples. Salt plates are stored in a desiccator in this same area.

The decoupled carbon-13 nmr spectra are included here for your use. They can be photocopied and handed out. The chemical shifts are given, along with the observed pattern when the carbon is coupled to protons (OFR): singlet (s), doublet (d), triplet (t) and quartet (q). The spectra were all obtained from actual student prepared samples, and they all "clean" except for the product derived from cumene.

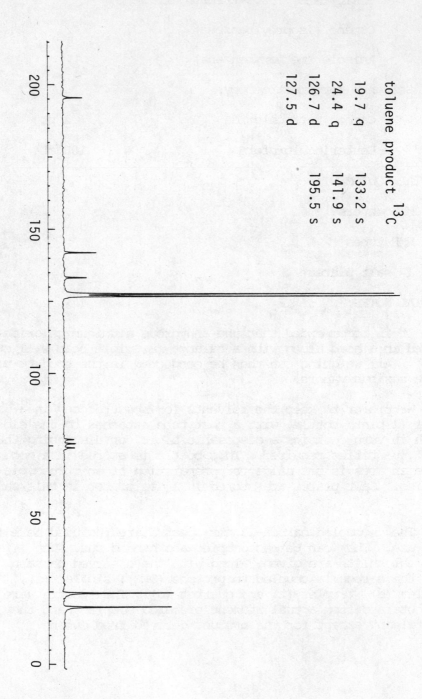

toluene product ^{13}C

19.7 q   133.2 s
24.4 q   141.9 s
126.7 d   195.5 s
127.5 d

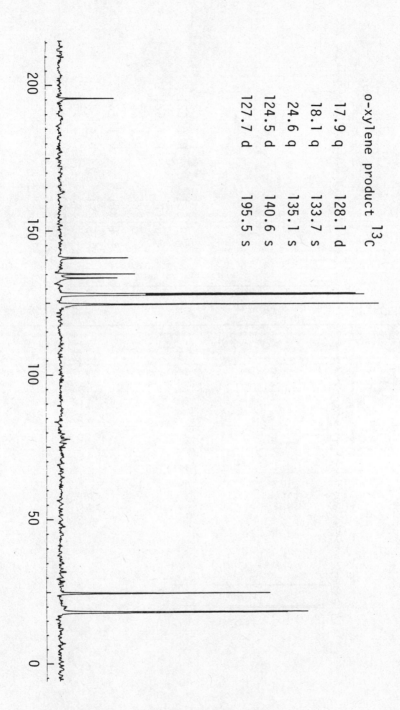

o-xylene product ^{13}C

17.9 q	128.1 d
18.1 q	133.7 s
24.6 q	135.1 s
124.5 d	140.6 s
127.7 d	195.5 s

87

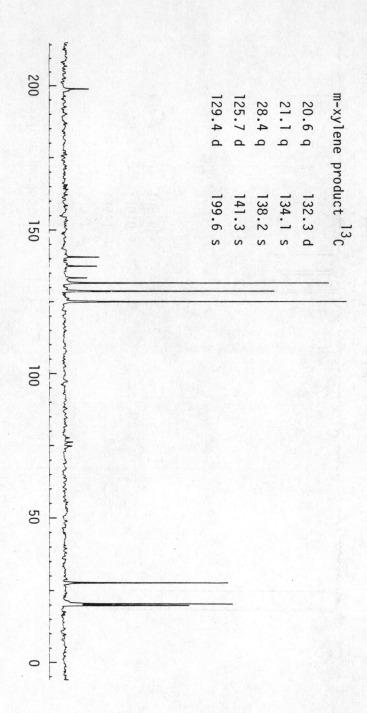

m-xylene product ^{13}C

20.6	q	132.3	d
21.1	q	134.1	s
28.4	q	138.2	s
125.7	d	141.3	s
129.4	d	199.6	s

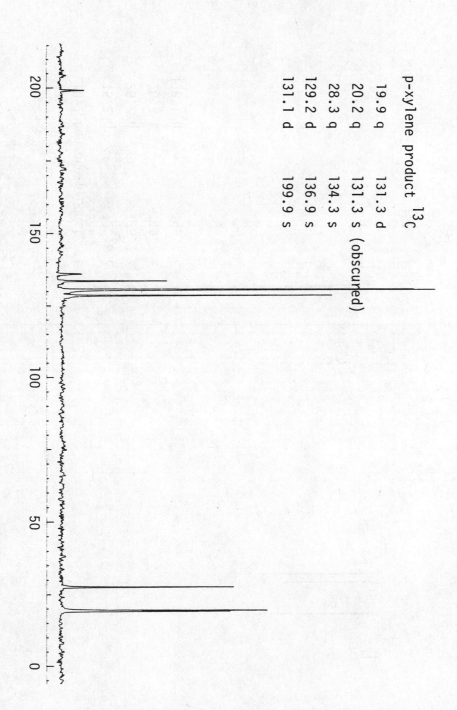

p-xylene product ^{13}C

19.9 q	131.3 d
20.2 q	131.3 s (obscured)
28.3 q	134.3 s
129.2 d	136.9 s
131.1 d	199.9 s

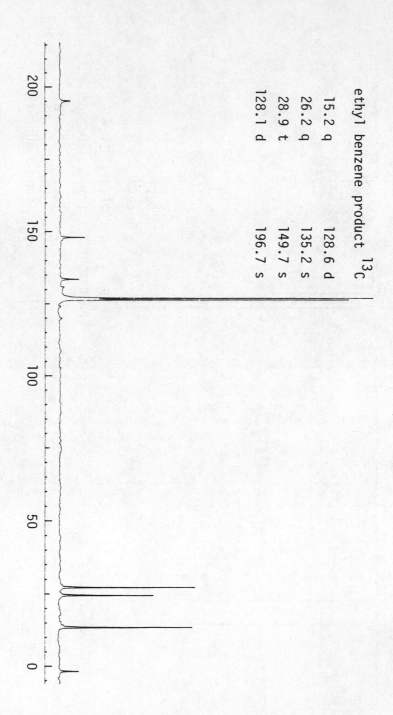

ethyl benzene product ^{13}C

15.2 q	128.6 d
26.2 q	135.2 s
28.9 t	149.7 s
128.1 d	196.7 s

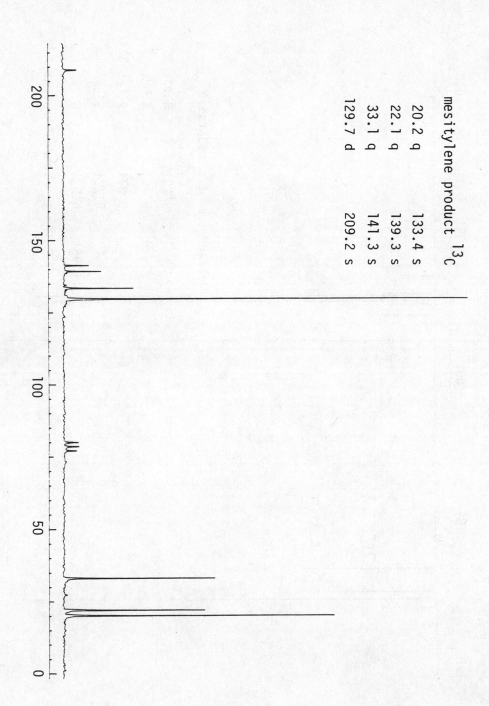

mesitylene product ^{13}C

20.2 q	133.4 s
22.1 q	139.3 s
33.1 q	141.3 s
129.7 d	209.2 s

91

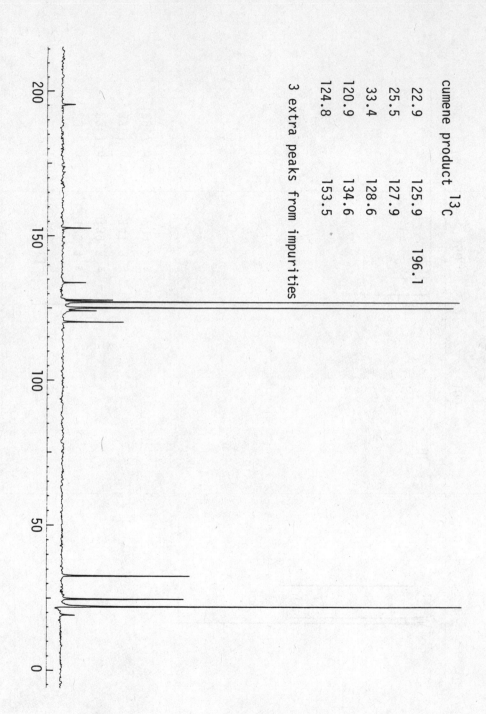

cumene product ^{13}C

22.9	125.9	196.1
25.5	127.9	
33.4	128.6	
120.9	134.6	
124.8	153.5	

3 extra peaks from impurities

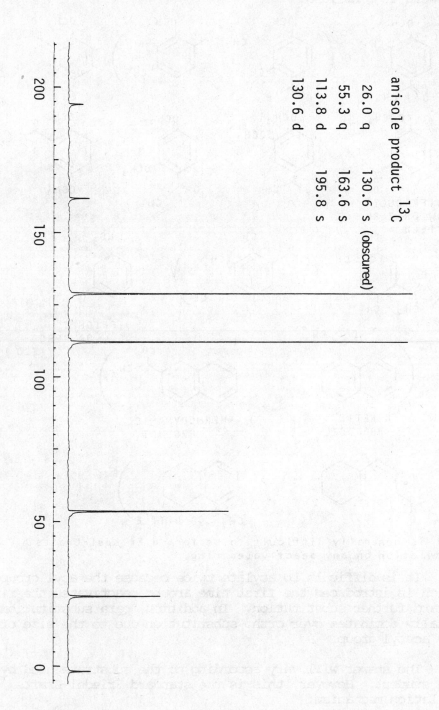

anisole product ^{13}C

26.0 q	130.6 s (obscured)
55.3 q	163.6 s
113.8 d	195.8 s
130.6 d	

ANSWERS TO QUESTIONS:

1.

*It is generally difficult to perform a Friedel-Crafts acylation on any deactivated ring.

2. It is difficult to acylate twice because the acyl group which is introduced the first time around deactivates the ring toward further substitution. In addition, _para_ substitution usually dominates over ortho substitution due to the size of the acetyl group.

3. The answer will vary according to the substrate used by the student. However, this is the standard Friedel-Crafts acylation mechanism.

4.   Meta directing groups deactivate the rings. In general, it is not possible to perform a Friedel-Crafts Reaction on a deactivated ring compound.

5.   The aluminum chloride causes a rearrangement of the propyl group to isopropyl. The Friedel-Crafts alkylation reaction is reversible

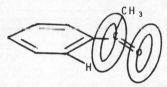

6. $AlCl_3 + 3 H_2O \longrightarrow Al(OH)_3 + 3 HCl$

   $CH_3COCl + H_2O \longrightarrow CH_3COOH + HCl$

7.   This is due to an anisotropic field originating from the pi electron cloud of the carbonyl group.

8.   In each case there will be one deshielded ring proton next to the acetyl group, while the other proton should be more or less normal. However, in the first case the second ring proton is para, while in the second it is meta. These would give different coupling constants.

Experiment 34

METHYL ORANGE

TIME ESTIMATE: 2 periods with purification and dyeing experiments included.

CHEMICALS AND SUPPLIES PER 10 STUDENTS:

   Sulfanilic acid, monohydrate   50 g

   Anhydrous sodium carbonate   15 g

Sodium nitrite	20 g
Dimethylaniline	30 mL
Glacial acetic acid	30 mL
10% Aqueous sodium hydroxide	500 mL
Sodium chloride	120 g
Saturated aqueous sodium chloride (36 g NaCl/100 mL H_2O)	120 mL
Conc. HCl	60 mL
Norit	
pH paper	

For the tests:

Multifiber fabric 10A

Available from:

Testfabrics Inc.	MINIMUM ORDER
P. O. Drawer O	1000 pieces
200 Blackford Ave.	$65/M (1979
Middlesex, New Jersey 08846	prices)

15% Aqueous sodium sulfate	125 mL
Conc. H_2SO_4	
Sodium carbonate	100 g
Sodium dithionite (sodium hydro-sulfite)	50 g

SPECIAL NOTES:

The amount of sodium hydroxide required to neutralize the acidic solution is frequently more than that specified in the experiment. The use of pH paper is recommended rather than litmus paper.

RESULTS:

Using Multifiber Fabric 10A, the following results were observed when treated with methyl orange:

Acetate - yellow
Cotton - pale yellow
Nylon - light orange
Dacron - no color
Orlon - no color
Wool - dark orange

Reduction with dithionite bleaches cotton more than the other fabrics.

ANSWERS TO QUESTIONS:

1. The dimethylamino group probably blocks the ortho position due to its steric bulk.

2.

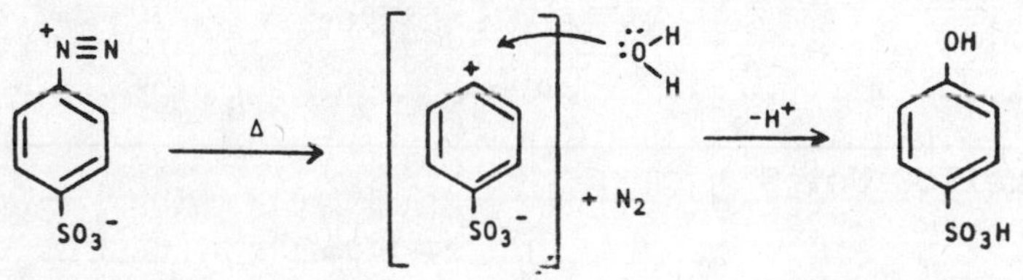

3. Sandmeyer Reaction

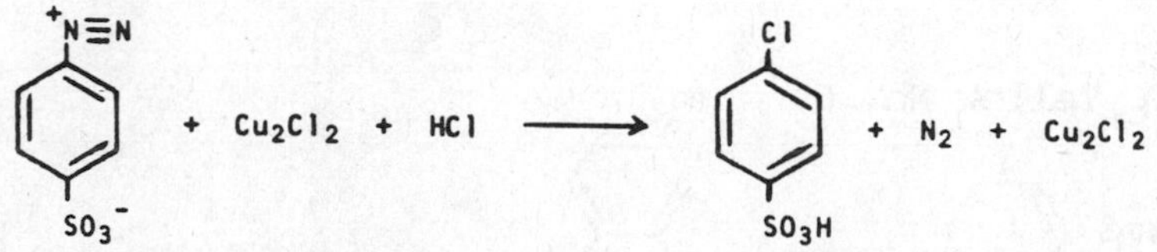

4.

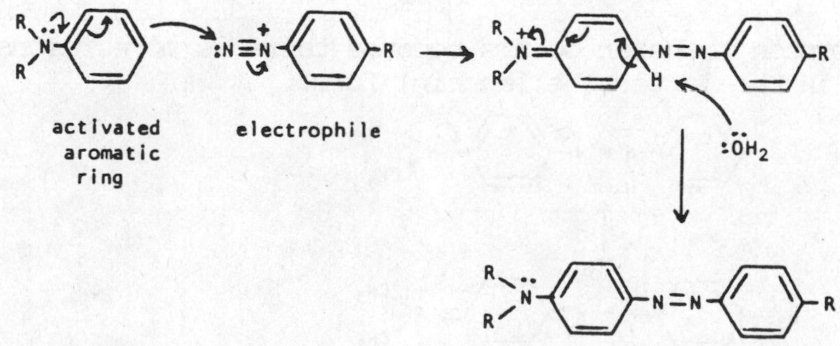

activated aromatic ring

electrophile

5.　FD & C Red No. 2

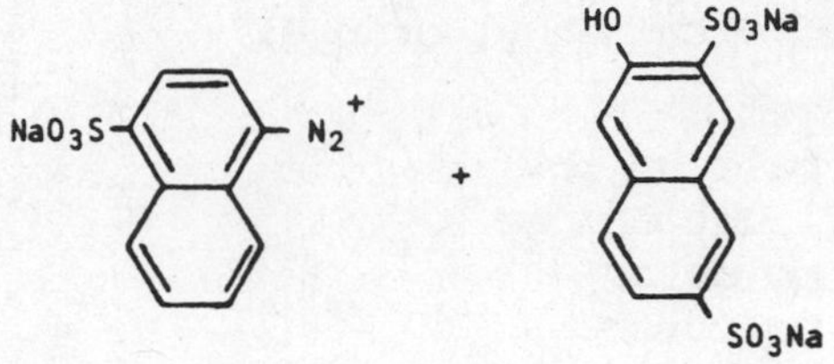

FD & C Red No. 40

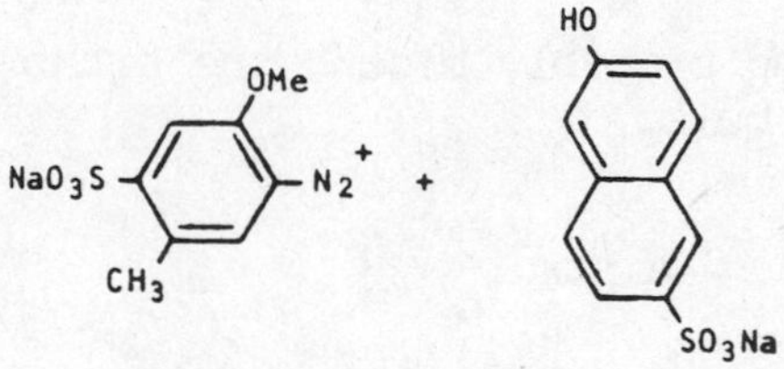

FD & C Yellow No. 5

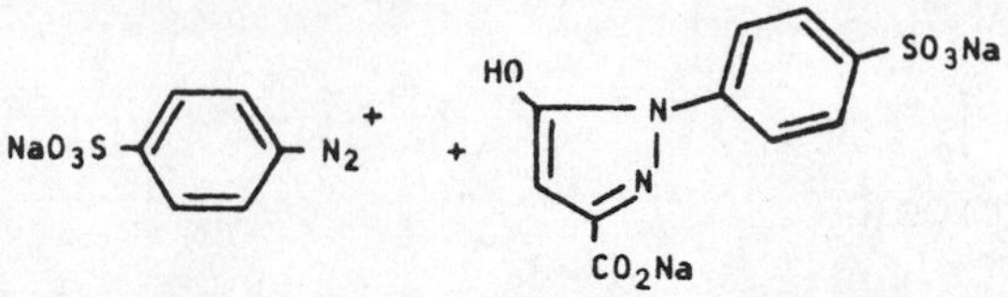

FD & C Yellow No. 6

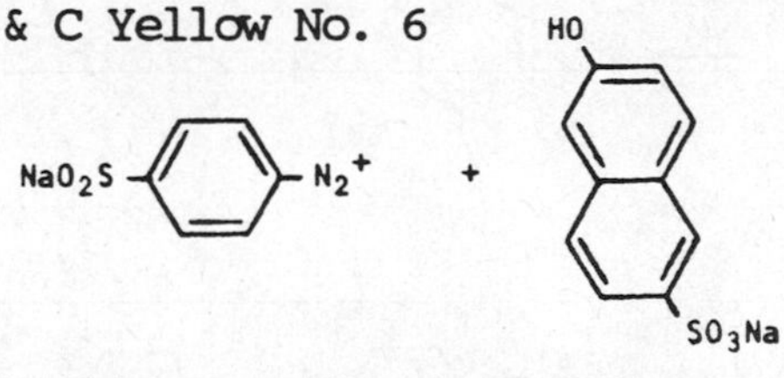

6.　The proton transfer occurs because there is more resonance possible in the latter (Helianthin) form:

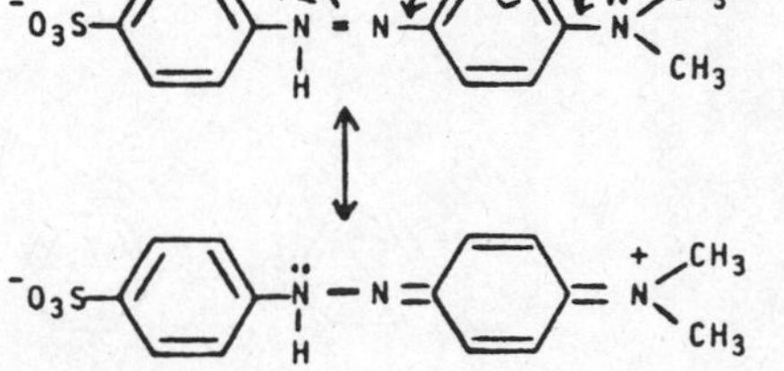

98

Experiment 35

DYES, FABRICS, AND DYEING

TIME ESTIMATE: 1 long period if multifiber fabric is used as recommended, 2 periods if fabric squares are used.

SUPPLIES AND CHEMICALS FOR <u>EACH STUDENT</u> (see also p. 264 of
Text)

Dyes (in small waxed envelopes)

Picric acid	0.5 g
Indigo powder	0.1 g
Congo red	0.1 g
Eosin	0.1 g
Alizarin	0.1 g
Methyl orange	0.1 g
Malachite green	0.1 g

This may seem like a lot of preparation, however, it is not necessary to weight these quantities exactly. We tell our lab assistants to weigh one or two samples, and then to estimate the remainder of the samples. Supplying "preweighed" samples prevents gross chaos at the balances during this laboratory.

Yarns

Pieces of wool yarn (10" long)   36

Preparing these samples is also not difficult with a little ingenuity. It can be done quickly using a 5 x 10" index card (several thicknesses). Just wrap the skein of yarn around the appropriate dimension counting the turns. Snip both ends and you will have a number of lengths equal to twice the number of turns. One 4 oz. skein of wool yarn will serve about 20-25 students. The wool should be

natural wool yarn and not white. White yarn has, of
course, already been dyed.

Fabric Pieces

If at all possible we encourage the use of multifiber fabric. This material saves an enormous amount of
time. Multifiber fabric 10A has the following materials
woven in sequence:

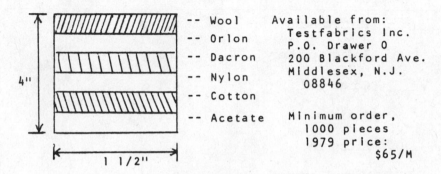

-- Wool   Available from:
-- Orlon   Testfabrics Inc.
                 P.O. Drawer O
-- Dacron   200 Blackford Ave.
-- Nylon   Middlesex, N.J.
                   08846
-- Cotton

-- Acetate   Minimum order,
                 1000 pieces
                 1979 price:
                           $65/M

Each student requires six pieces of Multifiber Fabric
10A. If material is used to prepare separate squares (2"
x 2") of each fabric, the following approximate amounts
of 45" width fabric are required:

Wool   (5 squares/student) = 1/3 yd/20 students

Cotton   (5 squares/student) = 1/3 yd/20 students

Polyester   (3 squares/student) = 1/3 yd/40 students

Nylon   (3 squares/student) = 1/3 yd/40 students

The material should be neutral color, undyed if
possible, and should have a soft finish. Material with a
hard finish is difficult to dye. Since many fabrics are
"sized", the material should be washed in warm soapy
water, and rinsed thoroughly, to remove the sizing.

Mordant Baths (1500 mL of each contained in 2 L beakers)

0.1 M Potassium aluminum sulfate (alum)

0.1 M Cupric sulfate (copper)

0.1 M Potassium dichromate (chrome)

0.1 M Stannous chloride (tin)

0.1 M Tannic acid

0.1 M Potassium antimony tartrate (tartar emetic)

The mordants should be kept warm on steam baths or hot plates. Each should be supplied with a glass rod for mixing. There should be about one bath of each mordant for every 15 students.

Other supplies per student:

Aluminum foil	1 12" square per student
Index card	1
String	
Sodium dithionite (sodium hydrosulfite)	0.5 g – 1.0 g
Sodium hydroxide pellets	1 ea.
10% Aqueous sodium carbonate	1 mL
10% Aqueous sodium sulfate	1 mL
p-Nitroaniline	1.5 g
10% Hydrochloric acid	6 mL
Sodium nitrite	0.8 g
β-naphthol	0.6 g
10% Aqueous sodium hydroxide	10 mL
Biphenyl	0.15 g
Liquid detergent (like Dreft)	

Experiment 36

CHROMATOGRAPHY OF SOME DYE MIXTURES

TIME ESTIMATE: 1-2 periods depending on which parts are assigned. Estimated times are given in the Text for each part.

SUPPLIES AND CHEMICALS:

I. PAPER CHROMATOGRAPHY OF FOOD COLORS

12 cm x 24 cm sheets of Whatman No. 1 filter paper	1 per student
32 oz. wide mouth screw cap jars (or Mason jars) for development chambers	1 per student
1-Pentanol (n-Amyl alcohol)	350 mL/10 students
Absolute ethanol	350 mL/10 students
Conc. ammonium hydroxide	50 mL/10 students
Several different brands of red, green, yellow and blue food colors	
Thin wall capillary tubing (open end)	
Microscope slides	1 box

Standards (0.1 g/20 mL H$_2$O)

F, D and C Red No. 2 Amaranth (Acid Red 27) C.I. 16185	EM AX0760	25 g
F, D and C Blue No. 1 Erioglaucine or Brilliant Blue C.I. 42090	EM EX0120	25 g

F, D and C Blue No.2
Indigo carmine
  C.I. 73015   EM IX0060   25 g

F, D and C Green No.3
Fast Green FCF
  C.I. 42053   EM FX0080   25 g

F, D and C Yellow No. 5
Tartrazine (Acid Yellow 23)
  C.I. 19140   EM TX0020   25 g

F, D and C Yellow No. 6
Sunset Yellow FCF
  C.I. 15985   P&B S12196   25 g

F, D and C Red No.3
Erythrosin B
  C.I. 45430   EM EX0135

F, D and C Red No. 40   Buffalo Color Corp.
Allura Red   W. Patterson, N.J.
                               07424

EM = Em Science (Formerly MCB)
P&B = PFALTZ and Bauer

II. PAPER CHROMATOGRAPHY OF THE DYES FROM A POWDERED DRINK
MIX OR A GELATIN DESSERT

The same supplies are required as for Part I. In
addition, the following are required:

Powdered Drink Mix (Kool Aid or other brand)

Several packages, assorted flavors:

black cherry	lime	strawberry
cherry	orange	and
grape	punch	others
lemon-lime	raspberry	

One package of each will serve a large class.

Gelatin Dessert (Jello or other brand)

Several packages, assorted flavors—see above

III. SEPARATION OF FOOD COLORS USING PRE-PREPARED TLC PLATES

Eastman Chromogram Sheets
No. 13180 or No. 13181

These come in a box of 20 sheets - enough to serve 160 students (80 students if two plates are used) when cut to 5 cm x 10 cm plates - use a paper cutter, being careful not to touch the surface.

Several different brands of red, green, yellow and blue food colors

2-propanol (isopropyl alcohol)   100 mL/10 students

Concentrated ammonium hydroxide   25 mL/10 students

Standard solutions of Red No. 40 (or Red 2), Blue No. 1, Yellow No. 5, and Yellow No. 6, dissolved in a minimum of water. See Part I for sources for these dyes.

8 oz. wide-mouth screw cap jars   1 per student
for development

Thin wall capillary tubing (open end) to make micropipets

IV. SEPARATION OF A DYE MIXTURE USING HAND-DIPPED TLC SLIDES

Several jars (4 oz.) containing a methylene chloride/silica gel G slurry (3 mL CH_2Cl_2 per gram silica gel G)

Methylene chloride (dichloromethane)
Silica Gel G

4 oz. wide-mouth screw cap jars for development chambers   1 per student

104

Filter paper to line development
    chambers

Thin wall capillary tubing (open
    end) to make micropipets

Microscope slides   4-5 per student

Unknown dye mixture:

    0.1 g Erythrosine (EX135)   All three
    0.1 g Fast Green FCF (FX80)   dissolved in
    0.1 g Sunset Yellow (SX1266)   20 mL methanol

This is enough for a very large class. See Part I
for sources for these dyes.

Standard dye solutions of single dyes (0.1 g/20 mL
    methanol) of

    FDC Red No. 2   Amaranth
    FDC Red No. 40   Allura Red
    FDC Blue No. 2   Indigo Carmine
    FDC Green No. 3   Fast Green FCF
    FDC Yellow No. 5   Tartrazine
    FDC Yellow No. 6   Sunset Yellow
    FDC Red No. 3   Erythrosin B

One bottle of 20 mL of each dye will suffice for a
very large class. See Part I for sources for these
dyes.

2-Propanol (isopropyl alcohol)   120 mL/10 students

Methanol   30 mL/10 students

Concentrated ammonium hydroxide   25 mL/10 students

V. SEPARATION OF A DYE MIXTURE USING PRE-PREPARED TLC PLATES

    Eastman Chromogram Sheets
        No. 13180 or No. 13181

    These come in a box of 20 sheets - enough to serve
    160 students (80 students if two plates are used)

when cut to 5 cm x 10 cm plates – use a paper cutter, being careful not to touch the surface.

4 oz. wide–mouth screw cap jars   1 per student
    for development chambers

Thin wall capillary tubing (open
    end) to make micropipets

Unknown dye mixture – see Part IV

Standard dye solutions – see Part IV

2–propanol (isopropyl alcohol)   100 mL/10 students

Concentrated ammonium hydroxide   25 mL/10 students

VI. SEPARATION OF A DYE MIXTURE BY COLUMN CHROMATOGRAPHY

Chromatography column made from   1 per student
    a 20 cm length of 10–mm glass
    tubing (see Text for details)

Glass wool

White sand

Tubing to fasten to column exit

Disposable pipets

Adsorption alumina   60 g/10 students

(We use Fisher A–540 Adsorption Alumina. The jar should be shaken thoroughly to mix the material. We have found that variation in particle size causes a variation in speed of material passing through the column; coarse alumina runs faster. Students should be encouraged to decant off the fine alumina prior to adding the slurry to the column. In this way, the coarser alumina will be used in the column. The alternative would be to buy a coarser grade of alumina.)

2–Propanol (isopropyl alcohol)   1 L/10 students

Concentrated ammonium hydroxide   200 mL/10 students

Ethanol (absolute)	200 mL/10 students
Methanol	200 mL/10 students
Unknown dye mixture – see Part IV	15 mL/10 students
Spectrophotometer cells (for UV/VISIBLE spectroscopy)	at least 2

If you choose to have the students monitor the column by tlc, or to identify the dyes, you will also need all the materials for either Part IV or Part V, depending on whether you wish them to use hand-dipped or pre-prepared tlc slides.

Experiment 37

ISOLATION OF CAROTENOID PIGMENTS FROM SPINACH

TIME ESTIMATE: 2 periods

CHEMICALS PER 10 STUDENTS:

Strained spinach (baby food)	120 g
95% Ethanol (or absolute ethanol)	150 mL
Methylene chloride	120 mL
Glass wool	
Sodium sulfate (anhydrous)	25 g

SUPPLIES REQUIRED FOR COLUMN CHROMATOGRAPHY:

Chromatography columns (see textbook for a detailed description)	
Ligroin (60-90°)	500 mL
Ethyl acetate	500 mL
Alumina (acid washed) (We use Fischer A-540)	125 g

107

| White sand | 50 g |
| Test tubes (small, 10 mL) | 12 per student |

SUPPLIES REQUIRED FOR THIN-LAYER CHROMATOGRAPHY:

Microscope slides (These must be carefully cleaned and dried, if they have been used previously.)	75
Silica Gel G Slurry Use methylene chloride as the solvent in preparing the slurry (3 mL CH_2Cl_2/ gram Silica Gel G). Use the same size jars as were used for the developing tanks.	1 jar
Wide mouth jars (for use as developing tanks)	10

OTHER SUPPLIES:

Iodine tanks	2
Open end capillary tubing	1 vial
Rulers with centimeter scale	2
Spectrophotometer cells (for UV/VISIBLE spectroscopy)	at least 2

ANSWERS TO QUESTIONS:

1.   Chlorophyll is less mobile than beta-carotene in both column and thin-layer chromatographies because chlorophyll is a more polar molecule than beta-carotene. Chlorophyll has a greater number of double bonds, and it possesses a far greater number of electronegative elements. These structural differences mean that chlorophyll, because of its greater polarity, will be more strongly adsorbed onto the alumina than beta-carotene would be.

2.   Lycopene would be expected to be less mobile than beta-carotene in a column chromatography experiment, because lycopene possesses a larger number of double bonds. As a

108

result, lycopene is more polar than beta-carotene, so it is adsorbed more strongly onto the alumina or silica gel.

3.   Lycopene has a more extended system of conjugated double bonds than beta-carotene. This longer chain of conjugation gives rise to adsorption of longer wavelengths of visible light. Lycopene absorbs light in the green region of the visible spectrum. beta-carotene absorbs light at a shorter visible wavelength, namely violet light. Since the color which the eye perceives is the complement of the color absorbed, lycopene appears red, while beta-carotene appears yellow.

Experiment 38

BENZOIN CONDENSATION

TIME ESTIMATE: 1 period

CHEMICALS AND SUPPLIES PER 10 STUDENTS:

95% Ethanol	1.5 L
Benzaldehyde	190 g

Air oxidation converts benzaldehyde to benzoic acid. A fresh bottle
should be used or else the benzaldehyde
should be distilled. If there is any
solid in the bottle, the benzaldehyde has
had considerable oxidation.

Sodium cyanide	19 g

We usually dispense this from a single
area (a hood) in the lab so that clean
up of spills is easy.

Be sure that students use the trap described in the experimental write up.
Under these conditions we have never
had any safety difficulties with this
reaction.

15% Aqueous sodium hydroxide for the gas traps	2 L

ANSWERS TO QUESTIONS:

1. The benzoin condensation is not possible with acetaldehyde as it has a α-hydrogens which are acidic.

$$CH_3CHO \; + \; :CN^- \; \rightleftharpoons \; ^-:CH_2CHO \; + \; HCN$$

Cyanide ion is, therefore, a strong enough base to induce a
base-catalyzed aldol condensation of acetaldehyde.

2.

Benzoin	Benzaldehyde
-OH 3200-3500 cm^{-1}	-CH aromatic 3080 cm^{-1}
-CH aromatic 3150 cm^{-1}	-CH aldehyde 2750 cm^{-1} and 2850 cm^{-1}
-CH aliphatic 2910 cm^{-1}	
C=O 1660 cm^{-1}	C=O 1705 cm^{-1}
C=C aromatic doublets near 1450 and 1580 cm^{-1}	C=C aromatic doublets near 1450 1600 cm^{-1}
C-O 1250 cm^-	

3.

Experiment 39

COENZYME SYNTHESIS OF BENZOIN

TIME ESTIMATE: 1 period

CHEMICALS AND SUPPLIES PER 10 STUDENTS:

Benzaldehyde   250 mL
   Should be free of benzoic acid impurity.
   Either use a new bottle, or distill this
   reagent before use. If the benzaldehyde
   has any solid in it, air oxidation has
   formed benzoic acid.

Thiamine hydrochloride (Vitamin B$_1$)   45 g
   It is a good policy to use freshly-opened
   bottles of thiamine for this experiment.
   The chemical seems to degrade with age.
   All thiamine should be stored in a refrig-
   erator when not in use.

95% Ethanol   1.5 L

2 M Aqueous sodium hydroxide   125 mL

SPECIAL NOTES:

Occasionally, the benzoin will form as an oil on cooling.
Scratching and cooling will usually induce crystallization. Alternatively, the solution may be heated to
redissolve the benzoin and then cooled more slowly.

ANSWERS TO QUESTIONS:

1.   See answer to Question 2, Experiment 38.

2.   To remove the HCl (i.e., to convert thiamine hydrochloride to the ylide)

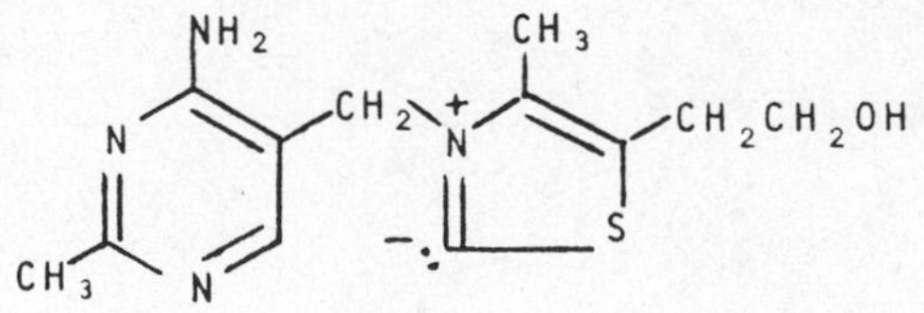

111

3.

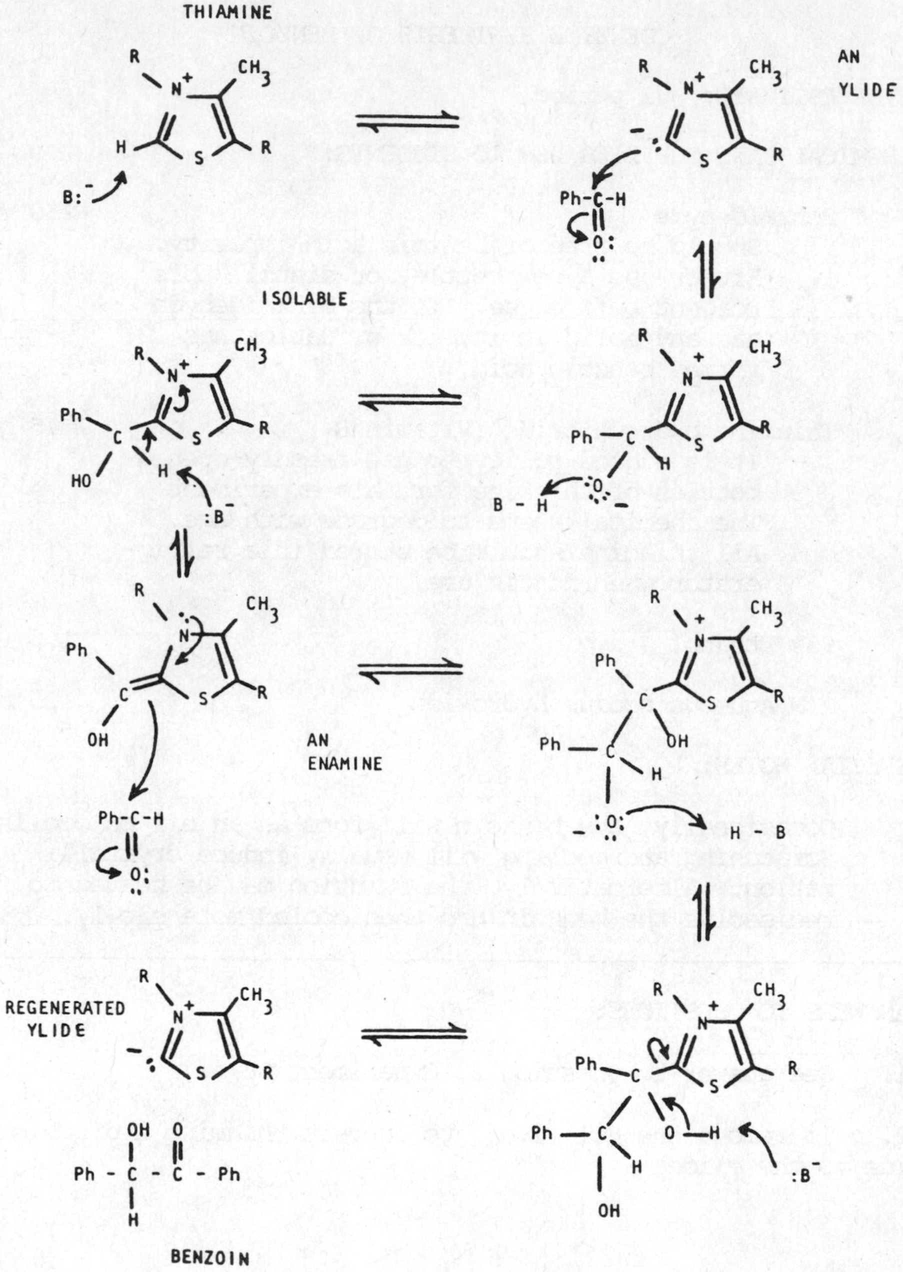

THIAMINE

AN YLIDE

R CH_3 N^+ H S R $B:^-$

R CH_3 N^+ S R $Ph-C-H$ $O:$

ISOLABLE

R CH_3 N^+ $Ph-C$ HO H S R $:B^-$

R CH_3 N^+ $Ph-C$ H S R $O:^-$ $B-H$

AN ENAMINE

R CH_3 N $Ph-C$ OH S R $Ph-C-H$ $O:$

R CH_3 N^+ Ph C S R $Ph-C$ OH H $O:$ $H-B$

REGENERATED YLIDE

R CH_3 N^+ S R

OH O $Ph-C-C-Ph$ H

BENZOIN

R CH_3 N^+ $Ph-C$ S R $Ph-C$ H OH $O-H$ $:B^-$

4.   It should have increased the yield, controlled the stereochemistry (benzoin is chiral), and allowed the reaction to occur under milder conditions. Additionally, less of the thiamin should have been required.

5.   Both temperature and pH would have to be controlled to avoid denaturation or destruction of the enzyme.

6.

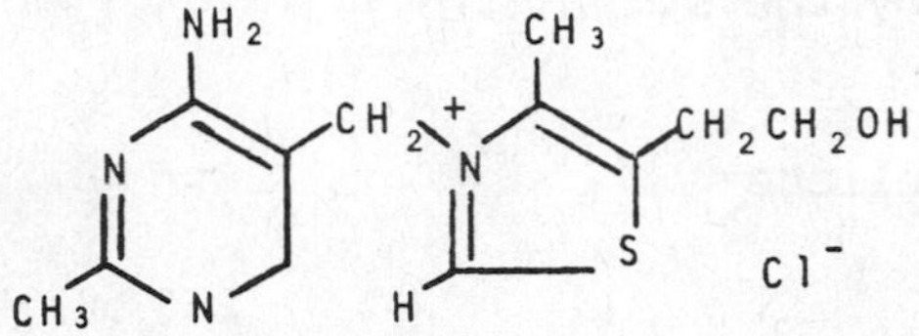

Experiment 40

BENZIL

TIME ESTIMATE: 1/3 to 1/2 period

CHEMICALS PER 10 STUDENTS:

Benzoin	125 g
Normally prepared by the student in Experiment 38 or 39.	
Concentrated nitric acid	625 mL
95% Ethanol	500 mL

SPECIAL NOTES:

This experiment is normally used in one of two multi-step sequences involving the following experiments:

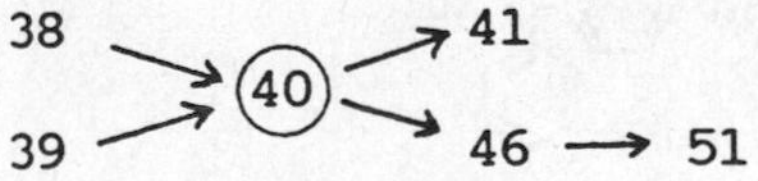

Experiment 41

BENZILIC ACID

TIME ESTIMATE: 1 period, or less

CHEMICALS PER 10 STUDENTS:

Benzil Usually prepared by the student in Experiment 40	70 g
Potassium hydroxide, pellets	70 g
95% Ethanol	250 mL
Decolorizing carbon	10 g
Conc. hydrochloric acid	
pH paper	

SPECIAL NOTES:

This experiment is the terminus of two possible multi-step sequences involving the following experiments:

38 → (40) → 41
39 ↗

ANSWERS TO QUESTIONS:

1. a)

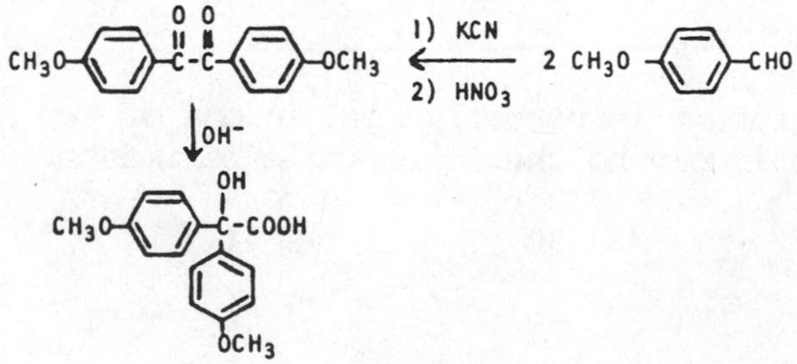

b)

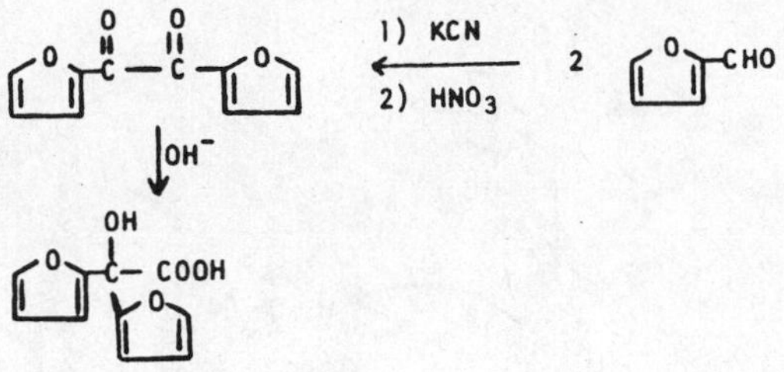

1) KCN
2) HNO$_3$

2   furan-CHO

OH$^-$

OH
furan—C—COOH
furan

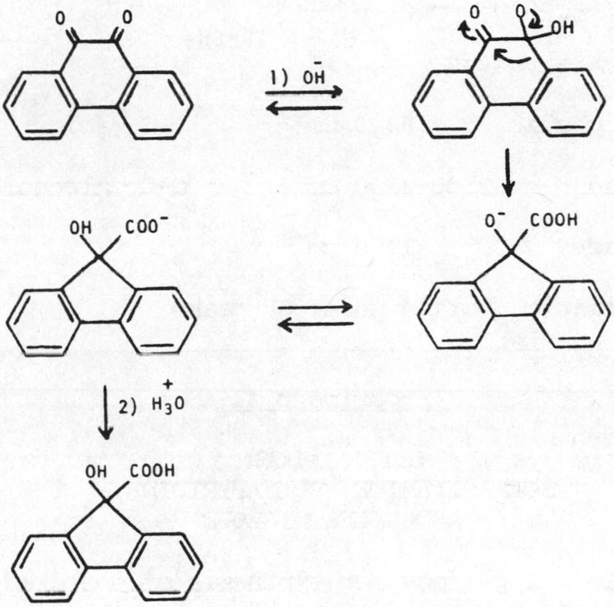

2. a)

1) OH$^-$

O$^-$ COOH

OH COO$^-$

2) H$_3$O$^+$

OH COOH

b)

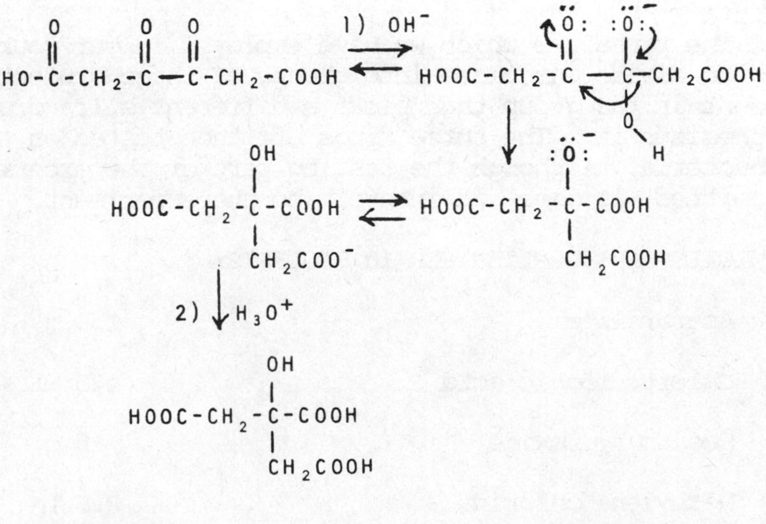

$$HO-C-CH_2-C-C-CH_2-COOH \quad \xrightarrow{1) \ OH^-} \quad HOOC-CH_2-C \text{—} C-CH_2COOH$$

OH
$$HOOC-CH_2-C-COOH \rightleftharpoons HOOC-CH_2-C-COOH$$
CH_2COO^- CH_2COOH

2) H$_3$O$^+$

OH
$$HOOC-CH_2-C-COOH$$
CH_2COOH

115

c)

$$\underset{\underset{\text{OCH}_3}{\big\downarrow}}{\overset{\overset{O}{\|}\;\overset{O}{\|}}{Ph-C--C-Ph}} \rightleftharpoons \underset{OCH_3}{\overset{\overset{O}{\|}\;\overset{O^-}{\|}}{Ph-C-C-Ph}}$$

$$\downarrow \qquad\qquad H-O-CH_3$$

$$\underset{\underset{Ph\;+\;CH_3O^-}{\big|}}{\overset{\overset{OH\;\;O}{\big|\;\;\|}}{Ph-C-C-OCH_3}} \xrightleftharpoons{} \underset{\underset{Ph}{\big|}}{\overset{\overset{^-O}{\big|}}{Ph-C-C}}\diagdown\overset{O}{}\diagup_{O-CH_3}$$

3.

OH	alcoholic	3400 cm^{-1}		C-O	acid
OH	acid	2500-3300 cm^{-1}		C-O	alcohol
C=O	acid	1700 cm^{-1}			
CH	aromatic, buried under OH peaks				

Peaks at 1150 and 1250 cm^{-1}

Experiment 42

SULFA DRUGS: SULFANILAMIDE, SULFAPYRIDINE, AND SULFATHIAZOLE

TIME ESTIMATE: 2 periods for synthesis of one drug, 1 additional period for testing the drugs

The procedure which we have employed in our courses has been to divide the class into groups of three students. Each student in the group then picks a different sulfa drug and synthesizes it. The three drugs are then tested on two kinds of bacteria. Although the testing part of the experiment can be omitted, it does add interest to the experiment.

CHEMICALS AND SUPPLIES PER 10 STUDENTS:

Acetanilide	150 g
Chlorosulfonic acid	425 mL (750 g)
Sodium hydroxide	15 g
Methylene chloride	2.5 L

116

500 mL Separatory funnels (if needed)

PROCEDURE 42A   (assume <u>entire</u> class does this experiment)

Conc. ammonium hydroxide	200 mL
6 N Hydrochloric acid	125 mL
Conc. hydrochloric acid	50 mL
Decolorizing carbon (Norit)	15 g
Sodium bicarbonate	50 g

PROCEDURE 42B   (assume <u>entire</u> class does this experiment)

2-Aminopyridine	30 g
Pyridine (dried over KOH pellets)	125 mL
10% Sodium hydroxide	250 mL
6 N Hydrochloric acid	250 mL
95% Ethanol	1.5 L

PROCEDURE 42C   (assume <u>entire</u> class does this experiment)

2-Aminothiazole	35 g
Pyridine (dried over KOH pellets)	125 mL
10% Sodium hydroxide	1 L
Conc. hydrochloric acid	500 mL
Sodium acetate	125 g

TESTING OF SULFA DRUGS ON BACTERIA (OPTIONAL)

INSTRUCTIONS FOR STUDENTS

The prepared sulfa drug may be tested on two types of bacteria: <u>Enterobacter aerogenes</u> and <u>Bacillus subtilis</u>. A group of three students should team up so that all three drugs are included on each plate. A specific area in the laboratory should be equipped for this experiment. Dissolve 0.25 g of

sulfanilamide or sulfathiazole in 70 mL of boiling distilled
water. Dissolve 0.25 g of sulfapyridine in a boiling mixture
of 50 mL of water and 20 mL of 95% ethanol.

While the drugs are dissolving, obtain agar plates which have
been pre-inoculated with the bacteria (see below for preparation of plates). The name of the bacteria has been written on
the top of the Petri dish. With a grease pencil divide the
bottom of the Petri dish into quadrants. In each quadrant
print one of the following symbols: SA (sulfanilamide), SP
(sulfapyridine), ST (sulfathiazole), or C (control). Place
the names or initials of the students in the group on the top
of the Petri dish.

Dip a pair of tweezers in 95% ethanol and place them in a
Bunsen burner flame to sterilize them. It is essential to
maintain sterile conditions at all times. The attitude that
contaminating bacteria are everywhere is a good one. The
bacteria tend to drop into solutions from above, but never
move up or sideways. After the tweezers have been sterilized,
dip two tabs into one of the sulfa drug solutions while it is
still boiling, and remove the tabs. Immediately place them
under a watch glass on a piece of filter paper to dry for a
few minutes. Again sterilize the tweezers and repeat the
above steps in succession with the two remaining solutions of
sulfa drugs. Finally, dip one tab in a beaker of boiling
distilled water. This tab serves as a control, since it does
not contain any sulfa drug. Lift the lid of a Petri dish
containing one of the bacteria, <u>straight up</u> so that it is
directly above the bottom. It should be lifted just high
enough to allow room for the tweezers. Insert the tweezers
with the control tab. Place this tab in the center of the
quadrant that was previously marked. Sterilize the tweezers
and transfer the tabs, in succession, to the center of the
appropriate quadrants on the agar plate. Repeat this opera-
tion with another agar plate containing the second bacteria to
be investigated. Again, care must be taken to avoid contamination of the bacteria. Once the tabs have been placed on the
plates, store the agar plates in one general area where the
temperature is maintained at 25 C. The plates should be
observed 24 and 48 hours after the introduction of the tabs.
During the first 24 hours, the drugs may have the greatest
growth-inhibiting effect. Thus, it is important to observe
the results at that time or before.

Holding the plates approximately level, observe the plates
from the bottom. The originally clear plates will be cloudy

118

in the area where bacteria has grown. Growth should be
observed around the control tab, but the agar will be clear in
the area where the sulfa drug has inhibited the growth of the
bacteria. One usually observes a clear circular area where
inhibition has occurred. The larger the circle, the greater
the effect of the sulfa drug in killing the bacteria. Inspect
all of the plates, not just your own group's plates. Sometimes the bacteria will not grow at all. If this has happen-
ed, the plate will be totally clear, even around the control
tab. Assess the relative effect of the three sulfa drugs on
each of the bacteria. Report the results to the instructor.

PREPARATION OF PLATES

The procedures given here are for the preparation of about 40
plates. There are enough plates to supply 60 students working
in groups of three and testing 2 bacteria. These procedures
can be followed by a laboratory assistant who has not completed a microbiology course, although it is preferred to have
the plates prepared by a microbiology student. The chemicals
and supplies are easily obtained from a biology stockroom or a
microbiologist. The bacteria used in this experiment are
relatively safe to use. Other similar experiments in the
literature use known human pathogens:

A. Krantz and R.G. Jesaitis, J. Chem. Ed., 50, 76 (1973)

G.L. Nelson and P.A. Buongiorno, J. Chem. Ed., 52, 676 (1975)

CHEMICALS AND SUPPLIES:

Peptone (Difco Labs #0118-01-8, available from suppliers)	15 g
Tryptone (Difco Labs #0123-01-1, available from Scientific Products, VWR, etc.)	18 g
Agar (Difco Labs #0140-01-0, available from suppliers)	15 g
Sodium chloride	16 g
Glucose	2 g
Inoculating loops	2

Bacteria slant (Bacillus subtilis, var. Niger)
Bacteria slant (Enterobacter aerogenes)

Cotton gauze for plugs

Bunsen burner

2 liter Erlenmeyer flasks	2
250 mL Erlenmeyer flasks	4

Disposable plastic petri dishes   40
    150 mm x 15 mm size are the best, but
    100 mm x 15 mm are satisfactory. These
    are available from Scientific Products
    and others (diSPo and Falcon #1058)

Filter paper discs (tabs)
    Schleicher and Schuell No. 740-E, 1/2 in.
    antibiotic discs; available from Scientific
    Products and others.

Disposable Serological pipet, 1 mL in 1/100 mL   4
    graduations, Kimble #56900

Glass "rake", described in Part IV   1

95% ethanol   500 mL

Shaker bath (30-35°)

Autoclave

Equip an area in the lab for use by the students.

PROCEDURE

The successful preparation of plates depends heavily on
correctly timing the related parts and on careful adherence to
sterile technique. A discussion of the proper timing is given
below and a discussion on sterile technique is given in Part
V.

An outline of the entire procedure follows:

  I Preparation of necessary solutions

Nutrient broth
Nutrient agar

II   Sterilization of solutions and plate preparation

III Preparation of cell suspensions in nutrient broth

IV   Inoculation of the plates

V   Notes on sterile technique

VI   Results of testing

The plates should only be made when everyone has their sulfa
drugs prepared and purified. A portion of a lab period is
reserved for placing the drugs on the pre-inoculated plates.

The preparation scheme that has been successful with us is as
follows: The morning of the day preceding the laboratory
period, the solutions are made and sterilized. The plates are
poured and stored in the refrigerator. The nutrient broths
are inoculated and incubated until the next morning. The next
morning the plates, which were prepared the preceding day, are
inoculated with the nutrient broth containing the bacteria.
These plates are then ready to use the day of the laboratory.

I   Preparation of necessary solutions

Nutrient Broth   Nutrient Agar

Peptone   15 g   Tryptone   10 g
Tryptone   8 g   NaCl   8 g
NaCl   8 g   Glucose   1 g
Glucose   1 g   Agar   15 g
Distilled water   Distilled water
to make 1 liter   to make 1 liter

Nutrient broth - This is a medium in which the bacteria
                 are allowed to grow and form a cell
                 suspension which is then used to
                 inoculate the nutrient agar plates.

Nutrient agar - This is the support and nutrient for
                 the bacteria while testing the effects
                 of the drugs. One liter of solution
                 makes about 40, 100 mm plates.

II Sterilization of solutions and plate preparation

The nutrient agar is autoclaved as indicated below in a large Erlenmeyer flask which is fitted with a cotton gauze plug. The nutrient broth is made as indicated in Part I and 125 mL portions of this solution are transferred to each of four 250 mL Erlenmeyer flasks (two flasks for each bacteria). The flasks are then fitted with cotton gauze plugs. These flasks are then autoclaved as indicated below.

The solutions should be autoclaved for about 15 minutes at about 120 C with pressurized steam (15 pounds pressure). The filter paper antibiotic discs (tabs) that will be used to carry the drugs must also be autoclaved in a glass petri dish. In addition, some disposable glass pipets with cotton plugs should be autoclaved after being wrapped in aluminum foil. Kimble disposable serological pipets may be used instead without being autoclaved.

The plates are then poured after the nutrient agar solution has been autoclaved being careful to use sterile techniques (See Part V). The liquid agar is removed from the autoclave and is allowed to cool before it is poured into the plastic petri dishes. The agar is cooled somewhat before pouring in order to prevent condensate from collecting on top of the petri dish. It is difficult to observe the zones on inhibition when the lid of the petri dish is fogged. The bottom of the dish is filled about one-half full with the agar. Do not allow the agar in the flask to solidify. Once the agar has been poured into the petri dish, the top is replaced, and the agar is allowed to cool and solidify. The poured plates can be stored for long periods as long as they are refrigerated in an air tight container. They can be prepared well in advance of the laboratory period.

III Preparation of cell suspensions in nutrient broth

The four flasks containing the nutrient broth are cooled to room temperature. Slants of the desired bacteria (Bacillus subtilis and Enterobacter aerogenes) are obtained along with a small amount of 95% ethanol, a burner, and an inoculating loop. For each bacteria two flasks of nutrient broth are inoculated in case that one does not grow. To inoculate the broth, the loop is placed in the alcohol, removed, and flamed. Using sterile techniques (See Part V) the cap is removed and some of the bacteria are scrapped off of the slant onto the loop. The nutrient broth is then tilted at an angle and its cap removed. Some of the bacteria on the loop are smeared in the flask at a point where it will be under the level of the solution when it is tipped back _after_ its cap has been replaced. The bacteria are burned off the loop and procedure is repeated with a new flask of nutrient broth.

In the case of Bacillus subtilis the flask should be swirled well so that there will be some cells on top of the solution. This is important because they are aerobic organisms while Enterobacter aerogenes are anaerobic.

The flasks are then put in a shaker bath which is controlled at 30 to 35°C. Within 12 hours the solutions should be cloudy. The Enterobacter aerogenes solutions will be white, while the Bacillus subtilis suspensions are orange. The cell suspensions have to be incubated (shaker bath) for 18 to 24 hours before they are used to inoculate the plates.

IV Inoculation of the plates

If the plates have been in the refrigerator they should be allowed to warm to room temperature before they are inoculated. The following procedures are then followed:

1. A long piece of glass rod is cut and shaped over a flame into a "rake". It should have a shape similar to that shown in the diagram. The handle should be made long enough so that the rake can be manipulated easily. The width should be about one-half the width of the petri dish.

2. A beaker is filled with 95% ethanol so that it extends 1 or 2 inches up the handle of the rake. 0.1 mL of the incubated nutrient broth containing the bacteria is pipeted onto the agar plates. The lid of the petri dish should be lifted only a few inches and straight up from the dish to prevent introduction of contaminants (See Part V). The top is replaced on the dish and the pipet is returned to the nutrient broth flask.

3. Next, the rake is removed from the ethanol and flamed until the alcohol has burned completely. The top of the petri dish is removed with one hand (1 or 2 inches) and the rake is used to evenly spread 0.1 mL of the nutrient broth over the agar surface. The top is replaced and the dish is turned 45°. Again, the top is removed and the surface is raked. The dish is turned and the surface raked in order to obtain an even

bacterial growth. The plate is turned and raked in 45°
increments until two or more complete 360° cycles have been
completed. The rake is returned to the ethanol.

4.   Steps two and three are repeated with another 0.1 mL
sample of nutrient broth on another agar plate. When one-half
of the agar plates have been inoculated with one bacteria, the
remaining plates are inoculated with the second bacteria. The
plates should be marked on top with initials (EA or BS) to indicate the bacteria contained in the petri dishes.

      After the plates have been inoculated with the nutrient
broth containing the bacteria, they should not sit out at room
temperature for more than 3 hours without being used with the
sulfa drugs. Procedures for testing the sulfa drugs are given
above under "Instructions for Students." The plates can be
stored after inoculation for up to 3 days at 15°C, but the
best results are obtained when they are used shortly after inoculation. Extra plates which have not been inoculated can be
stored for long periods as long as they are refrigerated in an
airtight container to prevent drying of the agar.

V   Notes on sterile technique

      The attitude that contamination bacteria are everywhere
is a good one. They tend to drop into solutions from above,
but never move up or sideways.

1.   Whenever one transfers anything from one sterile solution
to another, one must never let the solution be exposed in such
a way that there is a direct vertical path from the atmosphere
to the solution. It must therefore be tilted horizontally
before removing the cap and should always be horizontal while
the cap is off. After removing the cap, the mouth of the
container should be lightly flamed. This should be done
before replacing the cap. It should be flamed in such a way
that it will kill undesirable bacteria but not kill the
bacteria in solution.

2.   Whenever one opens a petri dish one must carefully lift
it so that it is directly over the bottom. It should be
lifted only the minimum distance and for the minimum time to
prevent contamination.

VI   Results of testing

      The results that the students obtain vary somewhat, but

the usual expectations are the following:

Enterobacter aerogenes
    Sulfanilamide does not inhibit or only slightly in-
        hibits the growth of the bacteria.
    Sulfapyridine inhibits the growth for 24 to 48
        hours, but begins to lose activity after that
        time. It is less active than sulfathiazole.
    Sulfathiazole inhibits the growth of bacteria up to
        and after 48 hours. It exhibits the best zone
        of inhibition of the three drugs.

Bacillus subtilis
    All of the drugs show activity and inhibit the
    growth of the bacteria; sulfathiazole > sulfapyri-
    dine > sulfanilamide

After the experiment is over, the plates should be collected
and autoclaved to kill the bacteria.

ANSWERS TO QUESTIONS:

1. $HOSO_2Cl$ + H_2O $\longrightarrow$ H_2SO_4 + HCl

2.   Since sodium hydroxide is a stronger base than sodium
bicarbonate it can remove one of the sulfonamide hydrogens to
produce a soluble ionic species. This would decrease the
yield.

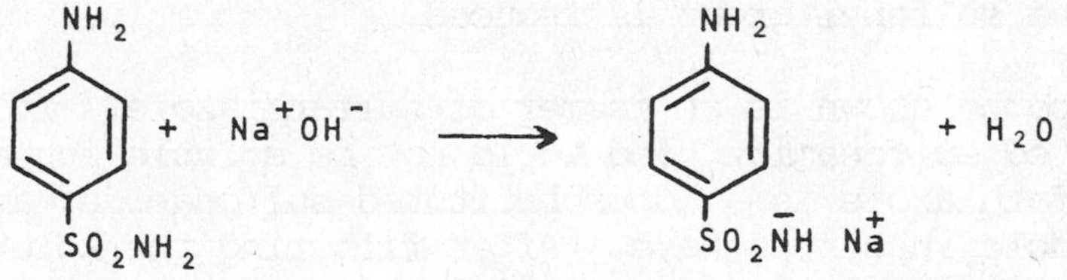

3.

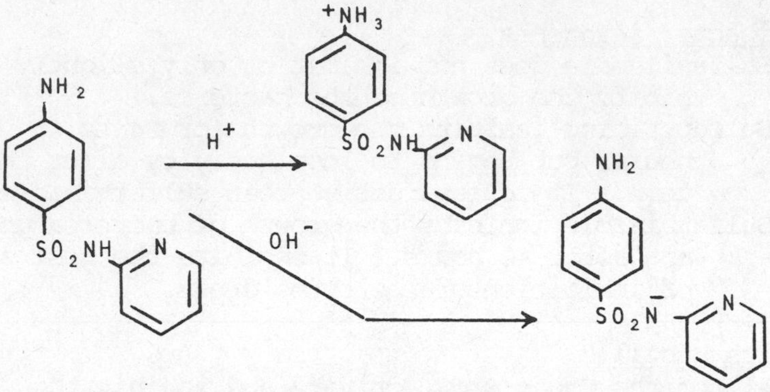

Ionic substances are produced in both acidic or basic solutions. Since these species are soluble, product will be lost. Sulfathiazole behaves in a similar manner.

4.

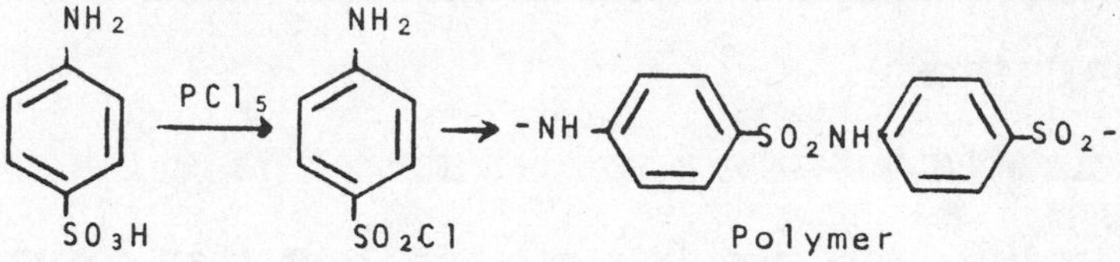

p-Acetamidobenzenesulfonyl chloride has the amino group protected with an acetyl group. This group reduces the nucleophilicity (by resonance) of the amino group, and its reactivity towards the sulfonyl group is reduced.

5. The compound shown is an isomer of sulfathiazole. It is a disubstituted sulfonamide, and would not be soluble in base. However, sulfathiazole is a monosubstituted sulfonamide, and would be soluble in strong base. After filtering the solution to remove the insoluble isomer, acidification of the filtrate would produce pure sulfathiazole.

Experiment 43

p-AMINOBENZOIC ACID

TIME ESTIMATE: 2 to 2 1/2 periods

CHEMICALS AND SUPPLIES PER 10 STUDENTS:

p-Toluidine	100 g
Hydrochloric acid (concentrated)	375 mL
Decolorizing carbon (Norit)	12 g
Sodium acetate trihydrate	150 g
Acetic anhydride	105 mL
Magnesium sulfate hydrate	315 g
Potassium permanganate	375 g
Celite	100 g
Ethanol (95%)	15 mL
Sulfuric acid (20% by weight) 21 g concentrated sulfuric acid/ 79 mL water	750 mL (May be prepared by the student)
Dilute aqueous ammonia 35 mL concentrated ammonium hydroxide/75 mL water	1.5 L (May be prepared by the student)
Acetic acid (glacial)	100 mL
1 L Beaker	10

ANSWERS TO QUESTIONS:

1.

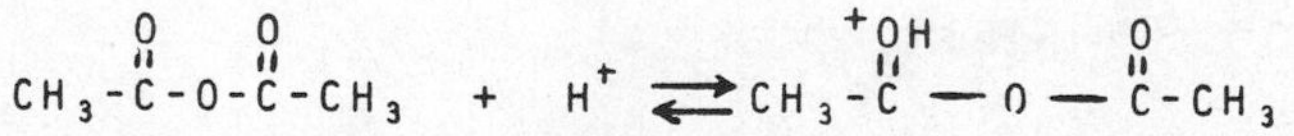

$$CH_3-\overset{O}{\overset{\|}{C}}-O-\overset{O}{\overset{\|}{C}}-CH_3 \;+\; H^+ \;\rightleftharpoons\; CH_3-\overset{^+OH}{\overset{\|}{C}}-O-\overset{O}{\overset{\|}{C}}-CH_3$$

127

The sodium acetate acts as a buffer to prevent the solution from becoming so acidic that the p-toluidine becomes protonated.

2. $$3 \ CH_3CH_2OH + 4 \ MnO_4^- \longrightarrow 3 \ CH_3\overset{O}{\overset{\|}{C}}-O^- + 4 \ MnO_2 + OH^- + 4 \ H_2O$$

3.

4. 3460 and 3370 cm^{-1} N-H stretch

2900 cm^{-1} (strong, broad) O-H stretch

1680-1600 cm^{-1} C=O stretch (split because of covalent and zwitterionic forms)

1580, 1520, 1440, and 1420 cm^{-1} C=C of aromatic ring

128

1300 cm^{-1} C-O stretch

840 cm^{-1} out-of-plane C-H bending

Experiment 44

BENZOCAINE

TIME ESTIMATE: This experiment requires one period or less, if the 2-hour reflux can be at least partly completed in the previous laboratory period.

The procedures for testing the benzocaine on a frog's leg muscle are given below. This should be done as a demonstration.

CHEMICALS PER 10 STUDENTS:

p-Aminobenzoic acid (prepared in Exp. 43)	65 g
95% Ethanol	850 mL
Conc. Sulfuric acid	65 mL
10% Sodium Carbonate solution	750 mL
Diethyl ether (solvent grade)	1.5 L
Magnesium sulfate (anhyd.)	40 g
pH Paper	

PROCEDURES FOR TESTING THE DRUGS ON A FROG'S LEG MUSCLE:

For added interest in the class, the student-prepared local anesthetics can be used to deaden a nerve. A frog's leg nerve-muscle segment can be used for the test since it is very sensitive to electrical stimulation and gives a strong response. The local anesthetic blocks the response of the muscle to electrical stimulation.

It is suggested that several leg muscle segments be prepared for a class demonstration. The muscles should be pre-

129

pared immediately before they are to be used. If the instructors have had no experience in the biological techniques of a physiology laboratory, it is strongly recommended that a knowledgeable student be recruited to prepare the leg muscle segments. Special care and handling of the excised muscle will be necessary. The leg muscle, once excised, should be kept moist in an isotonic saline solution, or "Ringer's solution." If the muscle dries, its response will be deadened.

It is recommended that the purest samples available (as judged principally by melting point and melting range) be selected for use in the tests. The local anesthetics must be utilized in the form of their hydrochloride salts. For benzocaine, which was not converted to its hydrochloride salt, it will be necessary to dissolve the weighed sample in enough dilute hydrochloric acid to provide a stoichiometric amount of hydrogen chloride before proceeding with the experiment.

PREPARATION OF THE LEG MUSCLE SEGMENT

The instructions given here will be adequate for a person trained in zoological techniques. A physiology laboratory manual should be consulted for those who are less experienced.

W. S. Hoar and C. P. Hickman, Jr., Laboratory Companion for General and Comparative Physiology, Printice-Hall, Englewood Cliffs, New Jersey (1967). This reference contains a series of pictorial drawings of the entire process.

Pithing the Frog. Prior to removing the leg muscle segment, the frog must be "double pithed." Hold the frog in the left hand with the mouth and nose between the first and second fingers and with the thumb on its back at the base of its neck. Using the dissecting needle, probe at the base of the skull until the depression there is located. Push the needle through this large opening, the foramen magnum, directly into the brain and rotate the needle to completely destroy the brain. Then, withdraw the needle partially and redirect its tip downward (caudally) through the vertebral canal to destroy the spinal cord. The hind legs of the frog should now be completely limp and flaccid and should also be unresponsive to any external stimulus like a prick with the needle.

Preparing the Leg Muscle Segment. During this procedure, care should be taken not to touch the exposed muscle or to allow it to dry. Care should also be exercised so as to not allow any of the frog's own blood to perfuse the exposed muscle or to allow any of the frog's outer skin or other injured tissue to touch the muscle. An isotonic physiological saline solution, or amphibian Ringer's solution, can be used to keep the muscle moist or to rinse it free from blood. Begin by cutting through the skin of the frog around the base of its abdomen and around the anus. Holding the frog by its head, peel the skin downward from the hind legs and remove it. Immediately rinse the exposed muscles in a tray containing an isotonic saline solution. Next, using a scissors, cut off the entire leg close to the pelvis. Cut away the thigh muscle and sciatic nerve, but leave a 1 cm length of the femus intact. Then, run the flat side of a scalpel blade under the Achilles tendon and cut it free at the base of the foot. Using a scissors, cut the tibio-fibula bone, which runs along behind the calf muscle, free near the knee joint. Store the leg muscle segment in a tray or beaker of fresh isotonic saline solution until it is needed.

TESTING THE LOCAL ANESTHETIC

Attaching the Muscle to the Stimulator. Using muscle clamp electrodes, attach the muscle to two clamps fixed to a ring stand. Attach the short length of the femur bone, not the muscle itself, to the upper clamp, and them clamp the end of the Achilles tendon to the lower clamp. DO NOT ATTACH THE CLAMPS TO THE MUSCLE ITSELF OR IT WILL BECOME INJURED. Be sure to keep the muscle moistened with isotonic saline solution at all times. It may be applied by means of an eyedropper. Next, correctly attach the electrodes by means of wires to the stimulator device. Use of a solid state electronic stimulator is recommended. A unit (Model No. 344), which includes complete instructions, is available from: Harvard Apparatus Co., 150 Dover Road, Millis, Mass. 02054. However, an induction coil attached by a key to a pair of dry cell batteries may also be used (Harvard Apparatus Model No. 308 Inductorium).

Testing the Local Anesthetic. Dissolve a small amount of the hydrochloride salt of the local anesthetic in the smallest possible amount of isotonic saline solution. Start the muscle contracting by the appropriate adjustment of the stimulating device. A rate of about 3 to 5 contractions per second should be established. Then, apply the solution of the local anesthetic dropwise using a capillary pipet or an eyedropper. If the drug is effective, the rate of contraction will decrease, and the muscle will actually cease to flex when a

sufficient amount of the anesthetic has perfused the muscle.
The muscle should not be flexed at too great a rate or for too
long a period prior to testing or it will become fatigued and
cease to function even before the local anesthetic is applied.

ANSWERS TO QUESTIONS:

1.

Infrared Spectrum	NMR Spectrum
3500 and 3400 cm^- N-H	1.4 (t) CH_3
3000 cm^{-1} C-H (under solvent peak)	4.3 (q) CH_2
1690 cm^{-1} conjugated C=O	4.0 (broad) NH_2
1620 to 1450 cm^{-1} aromatic C=C	6.5 and 7.8 RING
1600 cm^{-1} NH_2 bend	H's (para substituted)
1280 and 1170 cm^{-1} C-O	

Solvents peaks: 3030, 1220, 750 cm^{-1}

2.

$$\text{(benzene ring with } CO_2H \text{ and } NH_2) + H_2SO_4 \longrightarrow \text{(benzene ring with } CO_2H \text{ and } \overset{+}{N}H_3 \text{)} \quad HSO_4^-$$

3. Carbon dioxide is evolved:

from excess H_2SO_4: $H_2SO_4 + Na_2CO_3 \longrightarrow H_2CO_3 + Na_2SO_4$

$ \searrow H_2O + CO_2$

from benzocaine
salt:

$$\text{(benzene ring with } CO_2Et \text{ and } \overset{+}{N}H_3, \; HSO_4^-) + Na_2CO_3 \longrightarrow \text{(benzene ring with } CO_2Et \text{ and } NH_2) + H_2CO_3 + Na_2SO_4$$

$ \searrow H_2O + CO_2$

4. The solid formed during neutralization is sodium sulfate.
Benzocaine did not precipitate from the neutral solution
because it is soluble in the water/alcohol mixture.

132

5.

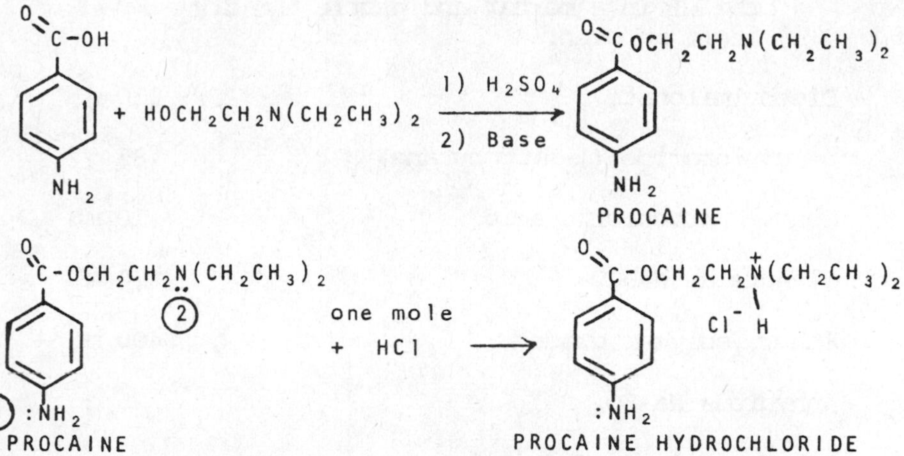

Position 2 will be protonated first because the nitrogen is more basic than the nitrogen at position 1. The nitrogen at 2 is a "normal" tertiary aliphatic amine (a localized pair of electrons), while the electron pair on the amino group at 1 is delocalized by resonance into the ring. This resonance effect decreases its basicity.

Experiment 45

5-n-BUTYLBARBITURIC ACID

TIME ESTIMATE: 2-3 periods

CHEMICALS AND SUPPLIES PER 10 STUDENTS:

DIETHYL-n-BUTYLMALONATE

Sodium metal   20 g
    We usually designate a hood to contain
    the sodium, which is stored under min-
    eral oil. Also provided in this hood
    is a triple beam balance, a shallow dish,
    a knife, and a waste container.

Absolute ethanol   300 mL
    Must be anhydrous. A freshly-opened
    bottle works well.

Powdered anhydrous KI   10 g
    The laboratory assistant should grind

the KI in a mortar and pestle and dry
it in an oven.

Diethylmalonate	110 g
n-Butylbromide (1-bromobutane)	85 g
Conc. hydrochloric acid	10 mL
5% Aqueous NaHCO$_3$	200 mL
Ether (solvent grade)	400 mL
Anhydrous Na$_2$SO$_4$	25 g

Anhydrous CaCl$_2$ for drying tubes

Manometers for the vacuum distillation

5-n-BUTYLBARBITURIC ACID

Sodium metal (see above)	15 g
Absolute ethanol (see above)	1.5 L
Urea	40 g

The urea should be oven dried, if
possible, but it is not essential.

Anhydrous CaCl$_2$ for drying tubes

Diethyl n-butylmalonate
As prepared in previous step

Conc. hydrochloric acid	100 mL
Petroleum ether (30-60°)	1 L

ANSWERS TO QUESTIONS:

1.   The by-product from the first step could easily be the
dialkylated ester, diethyl di-n-butylmalonate.

$$CH_2(COOEt)_2 \longrightarrow nBu-CH(COOEt)_2 \longrightarrow (nBu)_2C(COOEt)_2$$

2.   The sodium would react preferentially with the water in

either step (instead of the ethanol) forming the base sodium hydroxide, rather than sodium ethoxide.

$$2\ Na\ +\ H_2O\ \longrightarrow\ 2\ NaOH\ +\ H_2$$

$$2\ Na\ +\ EtOH\ \longrightarrow\ 2\ NaOEt\ +\ H_2$$

$$NaOEt\ +\ H_2O\ \rightleftharpoons\ NaOH\ +\ EtOH$$

Sodium hydroxide is a weaker base than sodium ethoxide and should be less effective in promoting either the alkylation or the condensation step. In addition, the water and hydroxide ion could initiate a hydrolysis of the ester groups:

$$CH_2(COOEt)_2\ +\ 2\ NaOH\ \longrightarrow\ CH_2(COO^-)_2\ +\ 2\ Na^+\ +\ 2\ EtOH$$

This cannot happen if the base used is sodium ethoxide.

Finally, in either step, the water could protonate the conjugate bases even if they were to form.

STEP 1

$$^-:CH(COOEt)_2\ +\ H_2O\ \rightleftharpoons\ CH_2(COOEt)_2\ +\ OH^-$$

STEP 2

$$NH_2(CO)-\overset{..}{N}H^-\ +\ H_2O\ \rightleftharpoons\ NH_2(CO)NH_2\ +\ OH^-$$

3. At the end of the condensation step, the conjugate base of the product is formed.

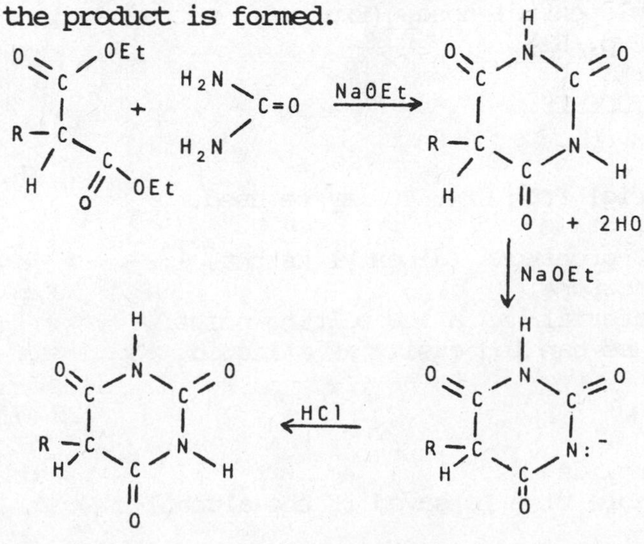

135

The conjugate base must be protonated and the excess of sodium ethoxide must be removed to neutralize the reaction mixture. For these reasons, hydrochloric acid must be added.

4. Diethyl n-butylmalonate

$2850-3000$ cm^{-1}	CH stretch	1360 cm^{-1} CH$_3$ bend	
1730 cm^{-1}	C=O stretch	$1000-1300$ cm^{-1} C-O stretch plus finger-	
1460 cm^{-1}	CH$_2$ bend	print	

5-n-Butylbarbituric acid

3250 and 3100 cm^{-1} NH stretch and probably OH stretch due to enolic tautomerism	1450 CH$_2$ bend	
	1350 CH$_3$ bend	
$1690-1780$ cm^{-1} various C=O stretch	1210 cm^{-1} possible C-O due to enolic forms	

Experiment 46

TETRAPHENYLCYCLOPENTADIENONE

TIME ESTIMATE: About 1 hour, if the recrystallization step is omitted. This is part of a multistep synthesis: Benzaldehyde to benzoin (Exp. 38, 39), benzil (Exp. 40), tetraphenylcyclopentadienone (Exp. 46), tetraphenyl-naphthalene (Exp. 51).

CHEMICALS PER 10 STUDENTS:

Benzil   30 g
     The material from Exp. 40 may be used.

1,3-Diphenyl-2-propanone (dibenzyl ketone, 1,3-
     diphenylacetone)   30 g
          This material has a low melting point.
          It can be handled easily as a liquid.

Absolute ethanol   225 mL

Potassium hydroxide   4 g
          Considerable time is saved if the alcoholic

potassium hydroxide solution is prepared by
the laboratory assistant. The solution must
be heated to dissolve the solid. (0.3 g/3 mL
alcohol)

95% Ethanol   250 mL

Toluene (if the solid is recrystallized)   75 mL

ANSWERS TO QUESTIONS:

1. C-H aromatic 3050 cm^{-1}
    C=O 1705 cm^{-1}
    C=C aromatic and olefinic 1601-1440 cm^{-1}

2. Aldol condensation:

$$\text{Ph-CH} \ + \ \text{CH}_3\text{C-PH} \xrightarrow{\ ^-\text{OH}\ } \text{PhCHCH}_2\text{C-Ph} \xrightarrow{\ -\text{H}_2\text{O}\ } \text{PhCH=CHCPh}$$

$$\overset{\|}{\text{O}} \qquad\quad \overset{\|}{\text{O}} \qquad\qquad \underset{\text{OH}}{|}\ \ \overset{\|}{\text{O}} \qquad\qquad\qquad \overset{\|}{\text{O}}$$

3. Aldol intermediate (A) and intermediate (B) shown on
pages 341 and 342. Also,

$$(\text{B}) + \text{Ph-C-CPh} \xrightarrow{\ ^-\text{OH}\ } \qquad\qquad + \ \text{ISOMERS}$$

Experiment 47

ENAMINE REACTIONS: 2-ACETYLCYCLOHEXANONE

TIME ESTIMATE: 2 periods
    In the first period, the enamine should be prepared and
    added to acetic anhydride. The second period is devoted
    to working up the reaction mixtures and distillation.

CHEMICALS AND SUPPLIES PER 10 STUDENTS:

Cyclohexanone   160 g

Pyrrolidine (keep in hood)   125 g

137

p-Toluenesulfonic acid monohydrate	3 g
Toluene	750 mL
Calcium chloride for drying tubes	25 g
Acetic anhydride (keep in hood)	170 g
Toluene	250 mL
3M Hydrochloric acid	1 L
Anhydrous magnesium sulfate	70 g
Manometers	

ANSWERS TO QUESTIONS:

1.   The mechanism for the enamine reaction resembles an acid catalyzed aldol condensation reaction (see a lecture textbook).   The $\Delta^{1,9}$-2-octalone product has a trisubstituted α,β-double bond in conjugation with the carbonyl group. The overlapping p-orbitals gives excellent stabilization to this compound.   On the other hand, the $\Delta^{9,10}$-2-octalone has a tetrasubstituted double bond, but it is not conjugated with the carbonyl group. Although more highly substituted double bonds are generally more stable in simple alkenes, the conjugation effect is more important with carbonyl compounds, and $\Delta^{1,9}$-2-octalone is the major product produced in the reaction.

2.   (a) In A, the pyrrolidine can be coplanar with the other ring which allows resonance stabilization to occur.   In B, the pyrrolidine ring cannot achieve coplanarity because of steric effects.   Since resonance stabilization cannot be achieved in B, it would not be formed easily.

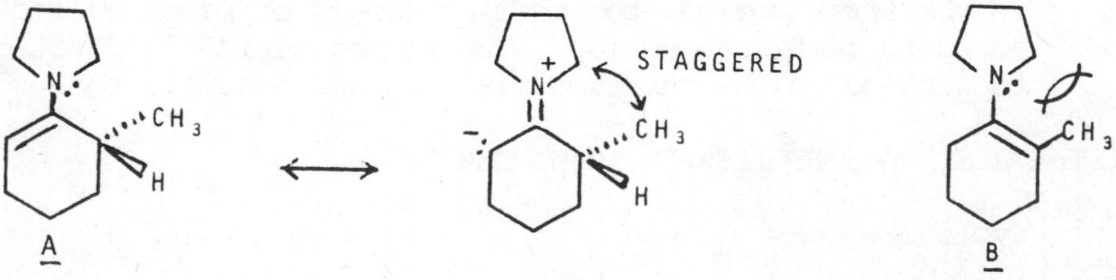

138

(b)

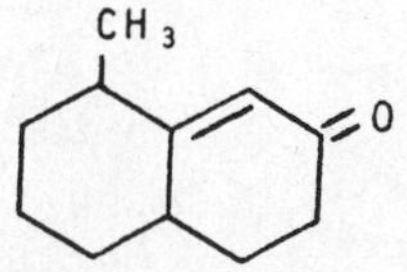

3.   (a)   The enolate corresponding to **A** in problem 2 is shown below.   It has a trisubstituted alkene structure.   Since trisubstituted alkenes are less stable than tetrasubstituted alkenes, it is less likely to form.   Notice that steric effects are not serious in _either_ enolate, as they were in the corresponding enamines (Problem 2).

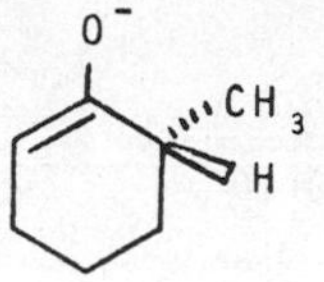

trisubstituted
"alkene"
(less stable)

tetrasubstituted
"alkene"
(more stable)

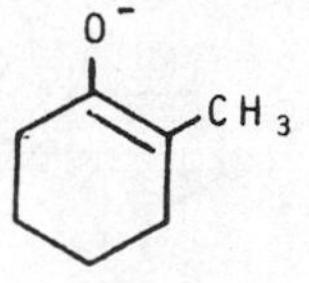

(b)

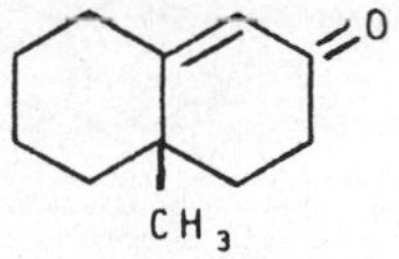

4.   (a)

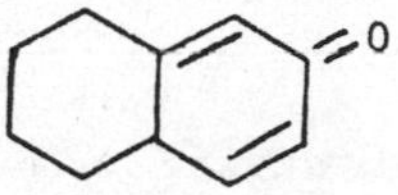

(b)

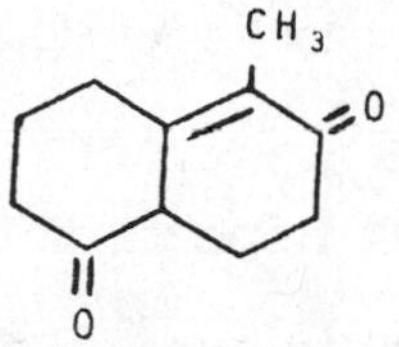

5.   (a)

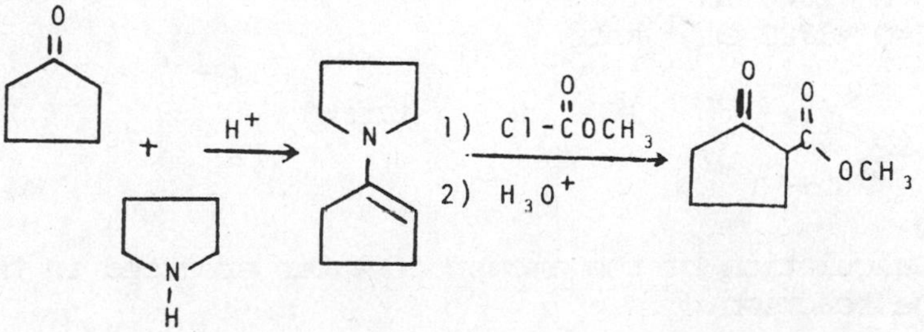

139

(b)

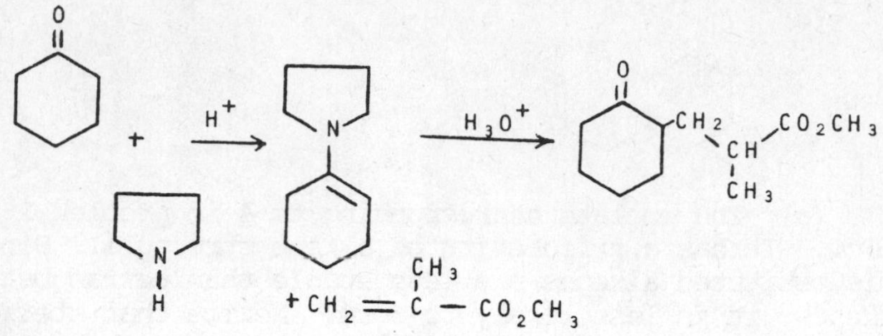

$+ CH_2 = \overset{\overset{\displaystyle CH_3}{|}}{C} - CO_2CH_3$

(c)

1) CH_3I
2) H_3O^+

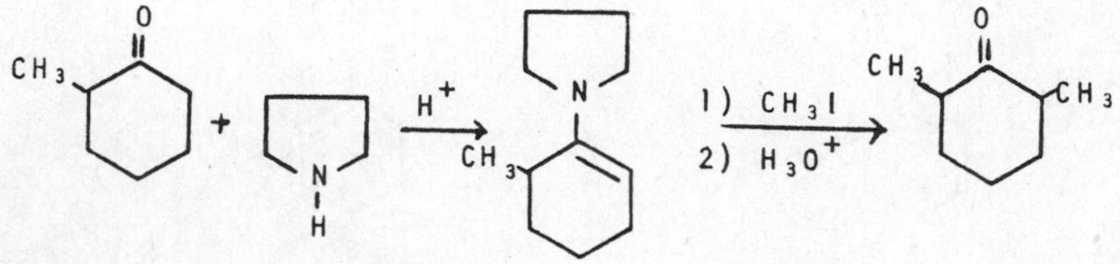

(d)

$+ CH_2 = CHCH_2Br$

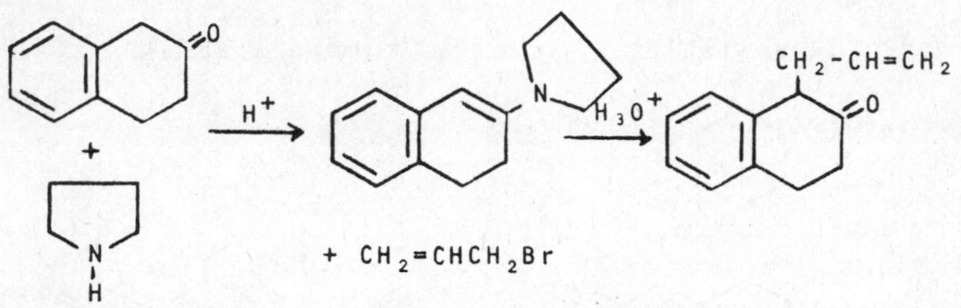

6. Infrared spectrum of 2-acetylcyclohexanone

O–H   3600–2400 cm^{-1} (broad)
C–H   2900 cm^{-1}
C=O   1720 cm^{-1} keto

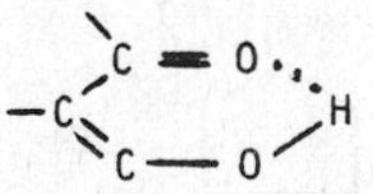

1600 cm^{-1} (strong)
enol

7. Calculation of the amount of water produced in the enamine reaction.

Moles of pyrrolidine = 0.132   Moles H_2O produced = 0.131
Moles of cyclohexanone = 0.131   g H_2O produced   = 2.36 g

8.

Experiment 48

THE ALDOL CONDENSATION REACTION: PREPARATION OF BENZALACETONE, BENZALACETOPHENONE AND BENZALPINACOLONE

TIME ESTIMATE: 1 period

There is considerable flexibility built into this experiment. Students may select one of the three procedures and a substituted benzaldehyde or one may be assigned to them. This experiment would be a good place to use carbon nmr spectroscopy, since the proton spectra are rather uninteresting. The aldol condensation reaction has been extensively reviewed: Organic Reactions, Vol 16, John Wiley, 1968, pp 1-444. It may be of interest to introduce other choices into the laboratory.

CHEMICALS PER STUDENT:

This experiment involves choices, and amounts of substituted benzaldehydes will need to be adjusted to fit the demand.

Piperonaldehyde (3,4-methylenedioxy-benzaldehyde)	1.9 g/student
Anisaldehyde (4-methoxybenzaldehyde)	1.6 g/student
3-nitrobenzaldehyde	1.9 g/student
Acetophenone	1.5 g/student
Pinacolone (3,3-dimethyl-2-butanone)	1.3 g/student
Acetone	12 mL/student

Sodium hydroxide	0.8 g/student
10% Aqueous sodium hydroxide	4 mL/student
95% Ethanol	11 mL/student

ANSWERS TO QUESTIONS:

1.
$$CH_3\text{-}\overset{\displaystyle O}{\overset{\|}{C}}\text{-}R \xrightarrow{\ ^-OH\ } \ ^-CH_2\text{-}\overset{\displaystyle O}{\overset{\|}{C}}\text{-}R \xrightarrow{\ Ar\text{-}\overset{\displaystyle O}{\overset{\|}{C}}H\ } Ar\text{-}\overset{\displaystyle OH}{\overset{|}{C}}H\text{-}CH_2\text{-}\overset{\displaystyle O}{\overset{\|}{C}}\text{-}R$$

$$\Big\downarrow\ ^-OH$$

$$Ar\text{-}CH=CH\text{-}\overset{\displaystyle O}{\overset{\|}{C}}\text{-}R \longleftarrow Ar\text{-}\overset{\displaystyle OH}{\overset{|}{C}}H\text{-}\overset{\_}{C}H\text{-}\overset{\displaystyle O}{\overset{\|}{C}}R$$

2.   The _trans_ isomer is thermodynamically more stable than the _cis_ one.

3.   The coupling constants for a _trans_ vicinal interaction is about twice as large as a _cis_ interaction. One can experimentally determine which isomer you have by use of the coupling constants.

4.   Acetone has acidic hydrogens on both sides of the carbonyl which gives dibenzalacetone. If the concentration of acetone is low, the first formed benzalacetone begins to undergo condensation at the methyl position. Acetophenone will not undergo the reaction with two moles of aldehyde since it only has acidic α-hydrogens on one side of the carbonyl.

$$Ph\text{-}\overset{\displaystyle O}{\overset{\|}{C}}H + CH_3\overset{\displaystyle O}{\overset{\|}{C}}CH_3 \rightarrow Ph\text{-}CH=CH\text{-}\overset{\displaystyle O}{\overset{\|}{C}}CH_3 \xrightarrow{\ Ph\text{-}\overset{\displaystyle O}{\overset{\|}{C}}H\ } Ph\text{-}CH=CH\text{-}\overset{\displaystyle O}{\overset{\|}{C}}CH=CH\text{-}Ph$$

                                  benzalacetone   dibenzalacetone

$$Ph\text{-}\overset{\displaystyle O}{\overset{\|}{C}}H + CH_3\text{-}\overset{\displaystyle O}{\overset{\|}{C}}Ph \longrightarrow Ph\text{-}CH=CH\text{-}\overset{\displaystyle O}{\overset{\|}{C}}Ph \xrightarrow{\ \times\ }$$

5. Acid and/or base catalyzed conditions are needed for each of the following reactions.

a)

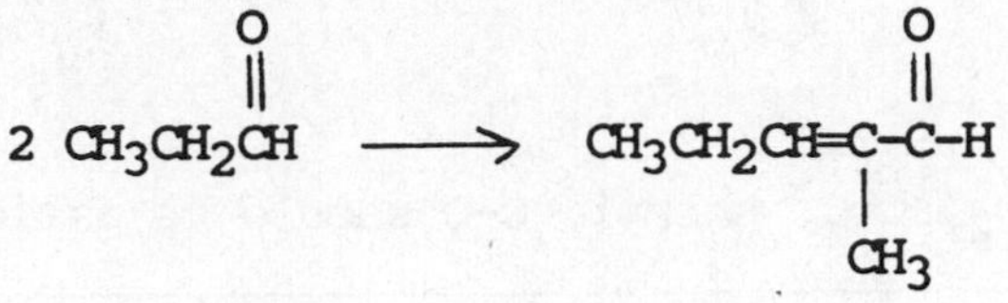

$$2 \ CH_3CH_2\overset{\overset{\displaystyle O}{\|}}{C}H \longrightarrow CH_3CH_2CH=\underset{\underset{\displaystyle CH_3}{|}}{C}-\overset{\overset{\displaystyle O}{\|}}{C}-H$$

b)

$$2 \ CH_3\overset{\overset{\displaystyle O}{\|}}{C}CH_3 \longrightarrow \underset{CH_3}{\overset{CH_3}{>}}C=CHC-CH_3 \quad (C=O)$$

c)

$$2 \ CH_3-\overset{\overset{\displaystyle O}{\|}}{C}-Ph \longrightarrow \underset{CH_3}{\overset{Ph}{>}}C=CH-\overset{\overset{\displaystyle O}{\|}}{C}-Ph$$

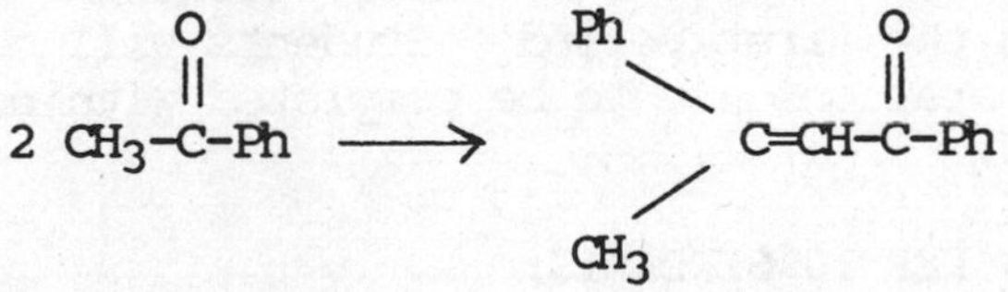

d)

$$2 \ CH_3O\text{-}\langle\bigcirc\rangle\text{-}\overset{\overset{\displaystyle O}{\|}}{C}H + CH_3\overset{\overset{\displaystyle O}{\|}}{C}CH_3 \longrightarrow CH_3O\text{-}\langle\bigcirc\rangle\text{-}CH=CH-\overset{\overset{\displaystyle O}{\|}}{C}-CH=CH\text{-}\langle\bigcirc\rangle\text{-}OCH_3$$

e)

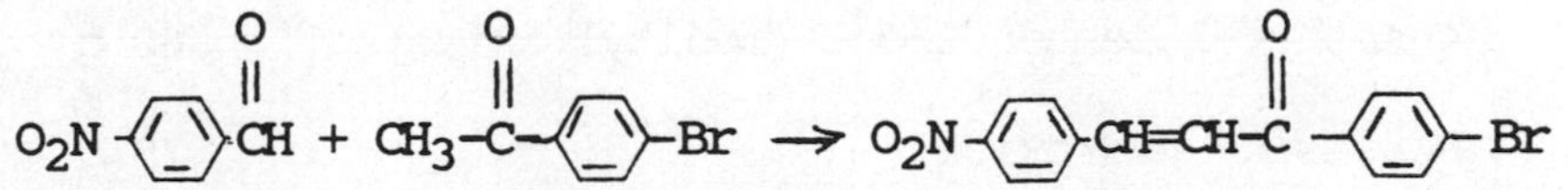

$$O_2N\text{-}\langle\bigcirc\rangle\text{-}\overset{\overset{\displaystyle O}{\|}}{C}H + CH_3\text{-}\overset{\overset{\displaystyle O}{\|}}{C}\text{-}\langle\bigcirc\rangle\text{-}Br \longrightarrow O_2N\text{-}\langle\bigcirc\rangle\text{-}CH=CH-\overset{\overset{\displaystyle O}{\|}}{C}\text{-}\langle\bigcirc\rangle\text{-}Br$$

f)

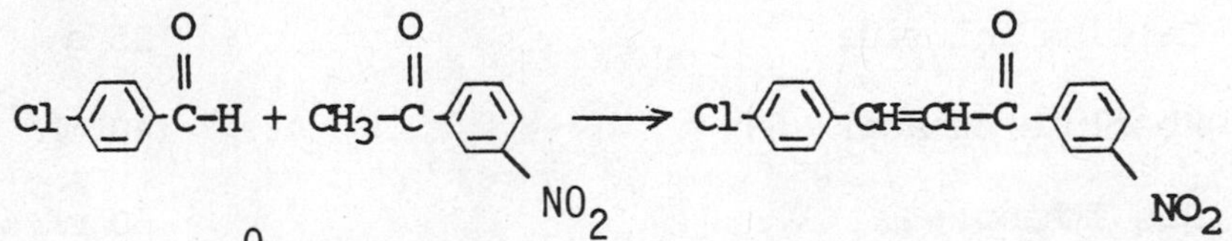

$$Cl\text{-}\langle\bigcirc\rangle\text{-}\overset{\overset{\displaystyle O}{\|}}{C}\text{-}H + CH_3\text{-}\overset{\overset{\displaystyle O}{\|}}{C}\text{-}\langle\bigcirc\rangle\underset{NO_2}{} \longrightarrow Cl\text{-}\langle\bigcirc\rangle\text{-}CH=CH-\overset{\overset{\displaystyle O}{\|}}{C}\text{-}\langle\bigcirc\rangle\underset{NO_2}{}$$

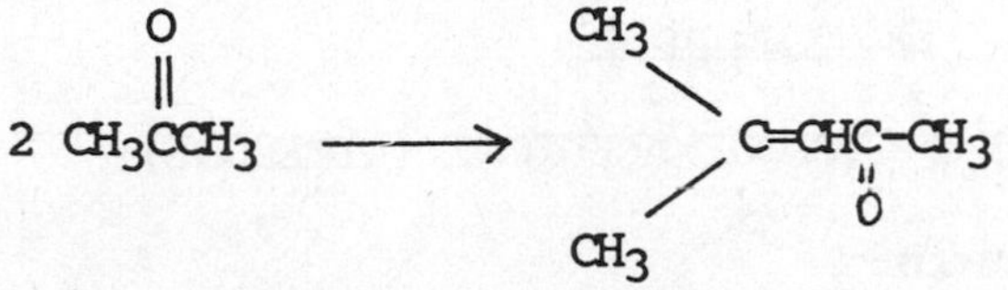

6.

143

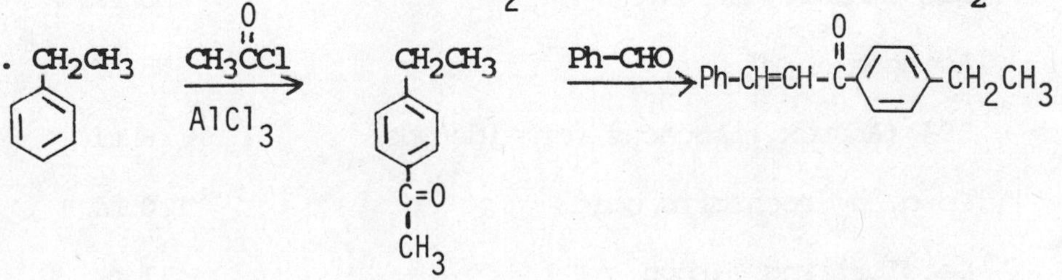

CH₃ (m-xylene) → [with CH$_3$CH$_2$C(=O)-Cl / AlCl$_3$] → acyl product → [with Ph-CHO] → Ph-CH=C-C(=O)- product

$$\text{m-xylene} \xrightarrow[\text{AlCl}_3]{\text{CH}_3\text{CH}_2\overset{\text{O}}{\overset{\|}{\text{C}}}\text{-Cl}} \text{(acylated xylene)} \xrightarrow{\text{Ph-CHO}} \text{Ph-CH=C}\underset{\text{CH}_3}{\overset{\|}{-}}\overset{\text{O}}{\overset{\|}{\text{C}}}\text{-(xylyl)}$$

7.   C=O Conjugated, NO₂, C=C, phenyl, C-O should be assigned.

Experiment 49

5,5-DIMETHYL-1,3-CYCLOHEXANEDIONE (DIMEDONE)

TIME ESTIMATE: 2 periods

There is a 1 hour reflux and several 0.5 hour operations that need to be done during the first period. Students will need to plan well if the operations are to be completed within a 3 hour laboratory period.

CHEMICALS AND SUPPLIES PER 10 STUDENTS:

Sodium metal	15 g
(Cut the metal into about 1.3 g blocks and store the pieces under xylene)	
Diethyl malonate	105 g
4-methyl-3-penten-2-one (mesityl oxide)	60 g
Potassium hydroxide	75 g
Calcium chloride	35 g
Absolute ethanol	240 mL
95% Ethanol	60 mL
Acetone	55 mL
38% (Approx.) Aqueous formaldehyde	6 mL
Conc. hydrochloric acid	120 mL
Decolorizing carbon	11 g

pH paper

Whatman #1 filter paper

STATION FOR STORAGE AND HANDLING OF SODIUM METAL:

One or more areas should be set aside in the laboratory where sodium is cut and weighed. The following should be placed there.

Precut 1.3 g blocks of sodium stored under xylene in a shallow wide-mouthed jar.

Xylene

Balance

Knife

Gloves

Tweezers

Paper towels

Petri dishes for student use in cutting and weighing sodium

Crystallizing dish <u>clearly labelled for sodium wastes</u>, filled with 1-butanol

---

ANSWERS TO QUESTIONS:

1.   a)
$$CH_3-\overset{\overset{\displaystyle O}{\|}}{C}$$
$$CH_3CH_2-O-\overset{\underset{\displaystyle O}{\diagdown\diagdown}}{C}$$
$$CH-CH_2CH_2-\overset{\overset{\displaystyle O}{\|}}{C}OCH_3$$

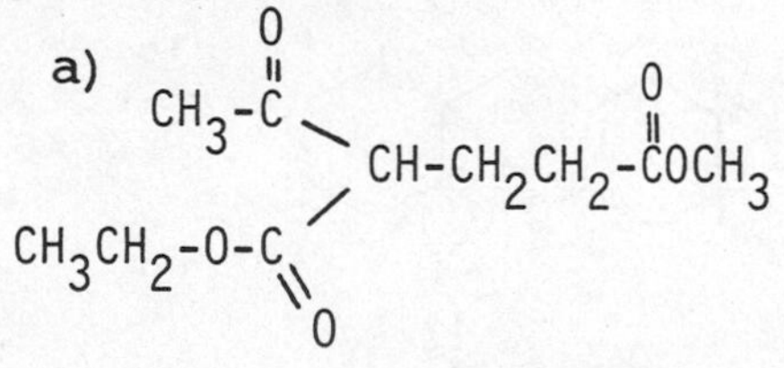

b)
$$CH_3CH_2-O-\overset{\overset{\displaystyle O}{\|}}{C}$$
$$N\equiv C$$
$$CH-CH_2CH_2C\equiv N$$

145

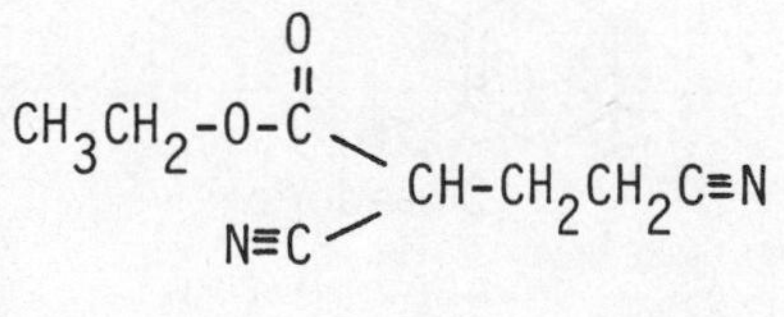

c) 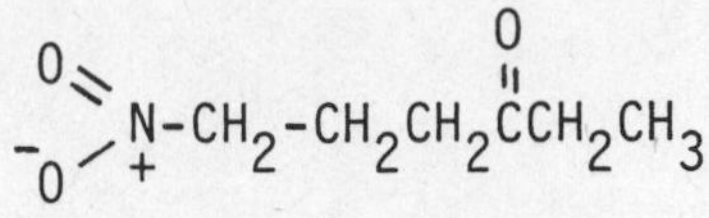 $O=\overset{-}{\underset{O}{N}}^{+}-CH_2-CH_2CH_2\overset{O}{\overset{\|}{C}}CH_2CH_3$

2. a) 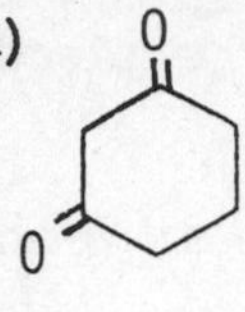 (structure)   b) 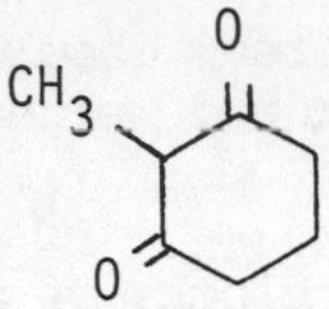 CH_3 (structure)

3. Sodium hydroxide would be produced in the reaction mixture if water is present in the alcohol. This would hydrolyze the ester functional groups in diethyl malonate, and this sodium salt could not participate in the reaction. The methylene hydrogens are not acidic.

4.

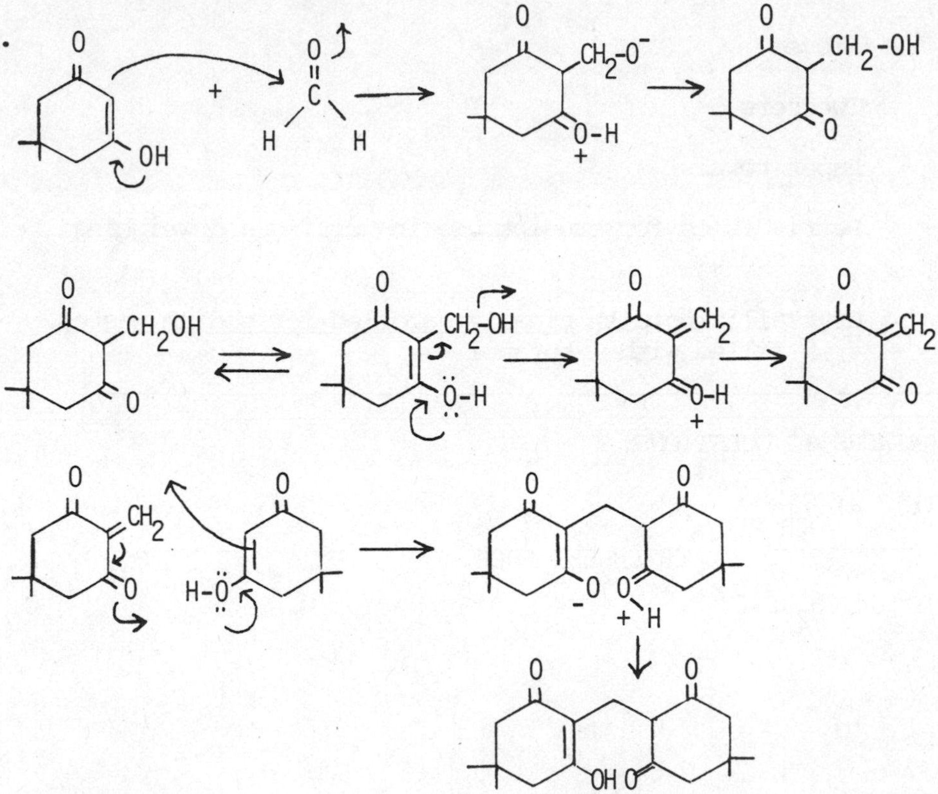

Dimedone

146

5.

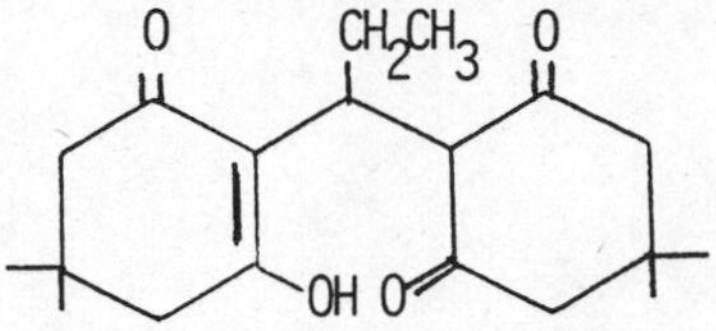

PREPARATION OF meso-TETRAPHENYLPORPHYRIN
AND SOME METALLOPORPHYRINS

TIME ESTIMATE: 1 period, excluding time required for
    ultraviolet-visible spectroscopy.

CHEMICALS PER 10 STUDENTS:

Pyrrole (this should be distilled before the class period)	75 mL
Benzaldehyde	100 g
Acetic acid (conc)	4.5 L
Methanol	250 mL
Copper(II) acetate	1 g (if everyone chooses this metal)
Iron(II) acetate	1 g (if everyone chooses this metal)
Nickel(II) acetate	1 g (if everyone chooses this metal)
Toluene	650 mL
Sodium sulfate (anhydrous)	25 g

SUPPLIES REQUIRED FOR UV/VISIBLE SPECTROSCOPY AND PREPARATION
OF METALLOPORHYRINS:

    UV cells

100 mL Volumetric flasks

25 mL Volumetric flasks

10 mL Pipets

Pipet bulbs

Experiment 51

BENZYNE FORMATION AND THE DIELS-ALDER REACTION: PREPARATION OF 1,2,3,4-TETRAPHENYLNAPHTHALENE

TIME ESTIMATE: 1 period, if the product is not analyzed by spectroscopy or recrystallized. Students should be cautioned about the evolution of carbon monoxide. Instructions for preparing a trapping agent for carbon monoxide are given in footnote 1, on page 380 along with an alternative apparatus.

This experiment is a part of a multistep synthesis: Benzaldehyde to benzoin (Exp. 38, 39), benzil (Exp. 40), tetraphenylcyclopentadienone (Exp. 46), tetraphenylnapthalene (Exp. 51).

CHEMICALS AND SUPPLIES PER 10 STUDENTS:

Tetraphenylcyclopentadienone   25 g
    The material from Exp. 46 should be used.

Anthranilic acid   10 g

Isoamyl nitrite (isopentyl nitrite)   20 mL
    Fresh material from Aldrich Chemical Co.
    is recommended (#15, 049-5). Store it in
    a refrigerator (see footnote 2, page 380 of
    the Text). We usually attach a pipet to the
    bottle for use in transferring the liquid.

1,2-Dimethoxyethane   475 mL

Methanol   250 mL

95% Ethanol (if needed for crystallization)   125 mL

Wooden applicator sticks   10

ANSWERS TO QUESTIONS:

1. Moles of CO = 1.9/384 g/mole = 0.00495 mole

    mL of CO = (0.00495)(22,400) = 111 mL at S.T.P.

2. a)   b)

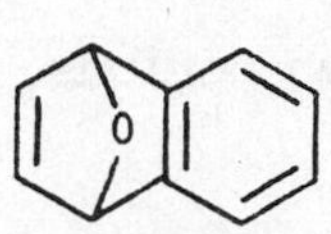

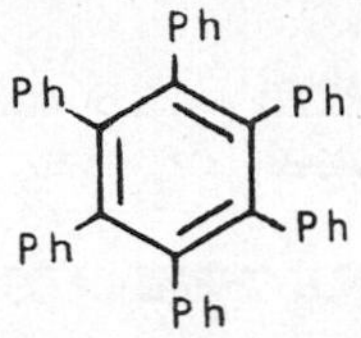

    c) 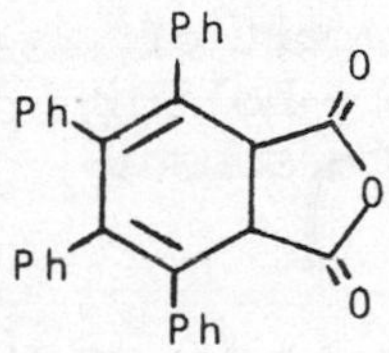   d)

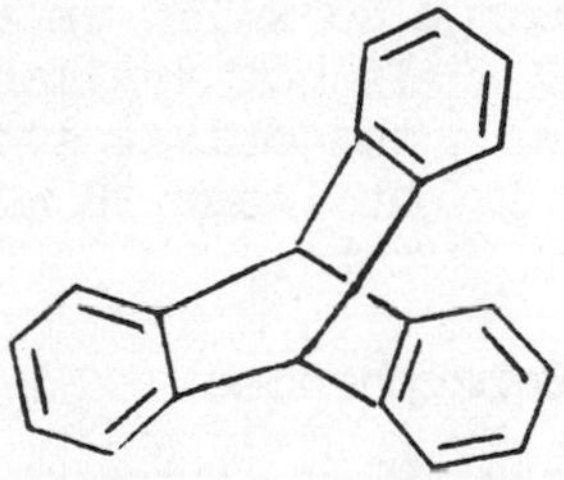

3. Infrared spectrum

    C-H aromatic,   3050 cm^{-1}
    C-H overtones, 2000-1650 cm^{-1}
    C=C 1600-1450 cm^{-1}
    C-H out-of-plane bending, 690 cm^{-1} and 750 cm^{-1} (under CCl$_4$)

4. nmr spectrum

    6.9δ 1,4-Phenyls (2,3-phenyls)
    7.3δ 2,3-Phenyls (or 1,4-phenyls)
    7.2-7.8δ Naphthalene ring hydrogens

5.

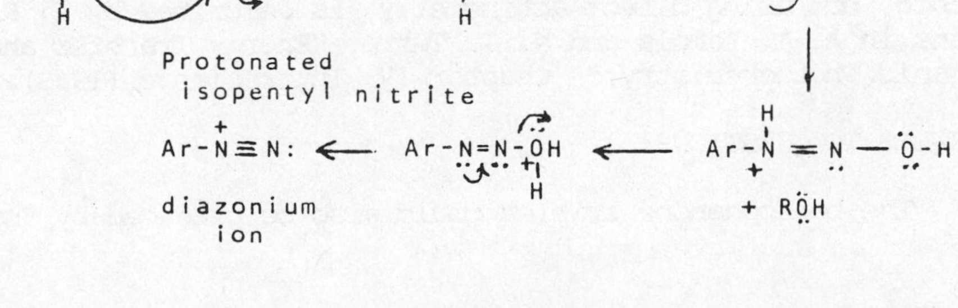

149

6.   As seen in the mechanism given in problem 5, the isopentyl group from isopentyl nitrite is converted to isopentyl alcohol.

Experiment 52

PHOTOREDUCTION OF BENZOPHENONE

TIME ESTIMATE: 15 minutes in each of two periods, separated by a week or two.

SUPPLIES AND CHEMICALS PER 10 STUDENTS:

Large 20 x 150 mm test tubes	20
If not available as a regular part of the drawer stock, any test tube holding at least 30 mL can be used as a substitute.	
Benzophenone	60 g
Naphthalene	5 g
2-Propanol (isopropyl alcohol)	750 mL

SPECIAL NOTES:

The amount of napthalene used to quench the reaction represents a huge excess. In fact, a useful modification of this experiment could be used by having each student use a different amount of napthalene (down to as low as, say 10^{-6} M, by powers of 10) and then to have the class as a whole compare results. In fact, if a method of evaluating the total amount of product (benzpinacol) is available (gas chromatography, column chromatography, etc.), a Stern-Volmer quenching plot of the $\emptyset q/\emptyset o$ type is possible without recourse to actinometry.

An experiment using actinometry is described by P. Natarajan (J. Chem. Ed., 53, 200, March 1956). A general method, not using direct actinometry, is described by T. R. Evans in A. A. Lamola and N. J. Turro, "Energy Transfer and Organic Photochemistry," Chapter IV, Interscience (1969).

ANSWERS TO QUESTIONS:

1.   The benzophenone triplet could also be produced by "sen-

sitization." In this approach, it would be necessary to excite a sensitizer molecule with a triplet state of higher energy than that of benzophenone. The higher energy triplet could then transfer energy to benzophenone.

2. The pinacol reduction could be written as a concerted reaction,

however, most references seem to feel it is a one-electron reduction of each carbonyl with a coupling of the radical anions.

Thus, in this reaction, the coupling occurs between two benzophenone radical anions, stabilized by magnesium, rather than between two diphenylhydroxymethyl radicals as in the photochemical reaction.

3. The benzophenone triplet, T_1, has a triplet energy of 69 Kcal/mole. The quenchers must have triplet energies lower than this value. Therefore, toluene and benzene may be immediately excluded as possible quenchers. Oxygen is a special case. It is already a triplet molecule in its ground state. With oxygen a different type of quenching occurs, called "triplet-triplet annihilation." To conserve spin, two singlets are produced.

$$Ph_2CO(T_1) + O_2(T_0) \longrightarrow Ph_2CO(S_0) + O_2(S_1) + energy$$

Oxygen may also interfere by radical addition reactions.

$$\underset{\underset{\displaystyle Ph}{}\diagup \overset{\displaystyle OH}{\underset{\displaystyle C}{|}}\diagdown \underset{\displaystyle Ph}{} \cdot \quad + \quad \cdot O\!-\!O \cdot \quad \longrightarrow \quad Ph - \overset{\displaystyle OH}{\underset{\displaystyle Ph}{C}} \diagup O - O \cdot$$

with ensuing difficulties.

Experiment 53

LUMINOL

TIME ESTIMATE: 1/2 period
This experiment may be co-scheduled with another short experiment.

CHEMICALS PER 10 STUDENTS:

3-Nitrophthalic acid	20 g

Aqueous hydrazine (10% by weight)
    Dilute 15.6 g commercial 64% hydrazine
    solution to a volume of 100 mL using water
	25 mL

Triethylene glycol	50 mL
Sodium hydroxide (10% by weight) 10 g sodium hydroxide pellets/90 mL water	100 mL
Sodium dithionite dihydrate (sodium hydrosulfite dihydrate)	50 g
Acetic acid (glacial)	50 mL
Potassium hydroxide pellets	350 g
Dimethyl sulfoxide	500 mL
Fluorescent dye	1 g

Examples of dyes which may be used include:

9-Aminoacridine	Rhodamine B
Eosin	2,6-Dichloroindophenol
Fluorescein	Phenophthalein
Dichlorofluorescein	

SPECIAL NOTES:

To observe the chemiluminescence, a darkened room should be made available. An alternative is to darken a hood by taping heavy butcher paper across the glass cover.

Experiment 54

cis, trans, and trans-1,4-DIPHENYL-1,3-BUTADIENE

TIME ESTIMATE: 2 periods or less, if the isomerization step and determination of UV spectra are omitted.

These optional experiments can be done by the instructor as a demonstration. The preparation of benzyltriphenylphosphonium chloride (Wittig salt) requires a 1.5 hr reflux. Other work may be scheduled during that period. Extra student prepared Wittig salt should be saved for future use as it is expensive to buy.

CHEMICALS AND SUPPLIES PER 10 STUDENTS:

Benzyl chloride (α-chlorotoluene)   46 g
   (Place in hood with balance)

Triphenylphosphine   134 g
   (Place in hood with balance)

p-Cymene   725 mL
   (Provide a container for collecting used
   solvent and redistill for future use)

Cinnamaldehyde   33 g

Magnesium sulfate   11 g

50% Aqueous sodium hydroxide solution   120 mL
   (Prepare a large quantity in ratio of
   50 g NaOH per 50 mL water)

60% Aqueous ethanol   880 mL
   (Prepare a large quantity in ratio of
   60 mL of 95% ethanol to 40 mL water)

95% Ethanol   330 mL

153

Silica gel plates with fluorescent indicator   20
    (Eastman No. 13181, cut up into 5 cm x 3
    cm strips)

Petroleum ether (30-60°)   82 mL

Methylene chloride (dichloromethane)   770 mL

SPECIAL EQUIPMENT:

UV lamp (1/class section)

Magnetic stirring unit (1/student)

Stirring bars (1/student)

OPTIONAL EXPERIMENT:

If time or equipment is a problem, the optional experiment may be done as a demonstration by the instructor. It
provides an excellent opportunity to demonstrate the use of UV
spectroscopy.

100 mL Volumetric flasks   4

10 mL Pipet   2

Pipet bulbs

Hexane   400 mL

Iodine   0.1 g

150 W Floodlamp

UV cells

ANSWERS TO QUESTIONS:

1. The cis, cis isomer could only be produced from cis-cinn-
amaldehyde by Wittig reaction. The trans isomer was used in
the experiment.

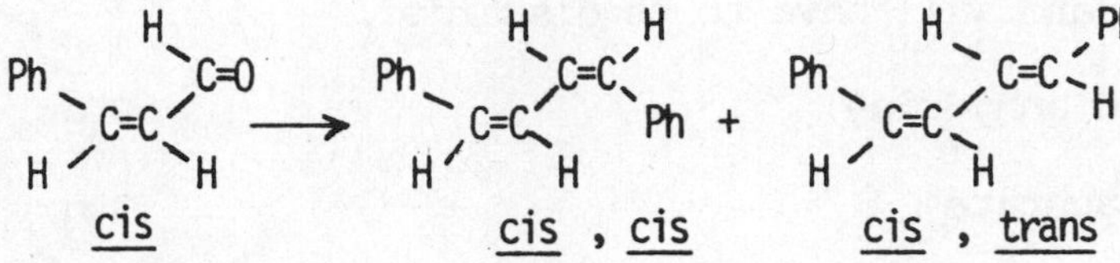

H
Ph   C=O
   C=C   →
H   H
cis

H   H
Ph   C=C
   C=C   Ph   +
H   H
cis , cis

H   Ph
Ph   C=C   H
   C=C
H   H
cis , trans

2. The steric effects are minimized by having the phenyl groups in the trans positions.

3. The rate of the bimolecular reaction is increased in the higher boiling solvent because of the higher temperature. More product is obtained in a shorter period of time.

4. 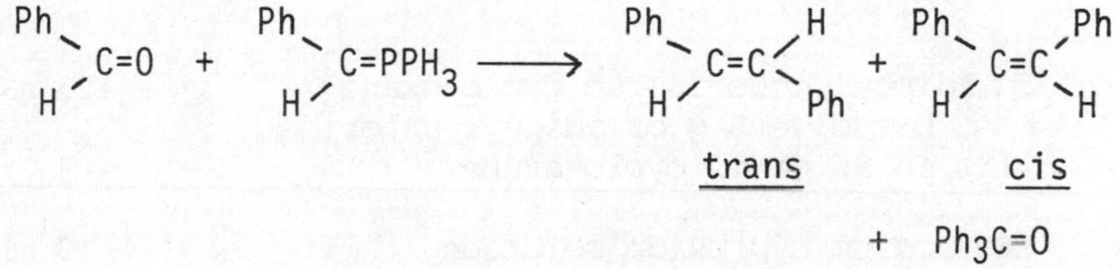 Ph
       C=O +
    H

Ph
   C=PPH$_3$ →
H

Ph   H
   C=C
H   Ph
trans

+

Ph   Ph
   C=C
H   H
cis

+   Ph$_3$C=O

5.

CH$_3$(CH$_2$)$_7$
             C=O +
    H

CH$_3$(CH$_2$)$_{12}$
             C=PPh$_3$ →
    H

CH$_3$(CH$_2$)$_7$ (CH$_2$)$_{12}$CH$_3$
             C=C
    H   H
          cis

+   trans

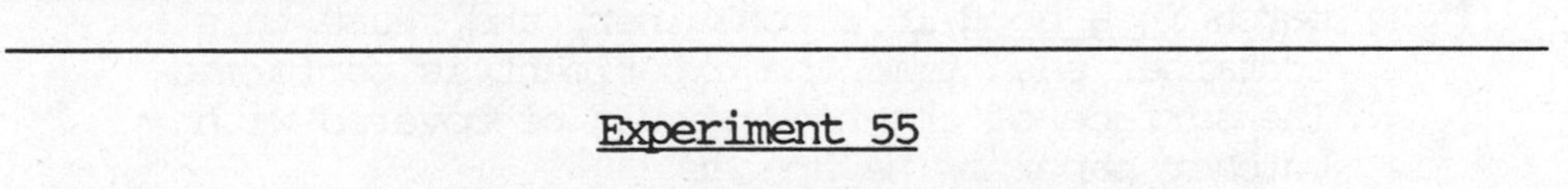

Some cis will be produced, but a considerable amount of trans will also be formed.

Experiment 55

PREPARATION OF POLYMERS: POLYESTER, NYLON, POLYSTYRENE AND POLYURETHANE

TIME ESTIMATE: 1 period

CHEMICALS AND SUPPLIES PER 10 STUDENTS:

<u>PROCEDURE 55A</u>
The test tubes used by the students cannot be cleaned and will have to be discarded.

Phthalic anhydride	50 g
Sodium acetate	3 g
Ethylene glycol	10 mL
Glycerol	10 mL

<u>PROCEDURE 55B</u>

5% Aqueous 1,6-hexanediamine (hexamethylenediamine) Dissolve 5 g of diamine in 95 mL of water.	125 mL
5% Adipoyl chloride in cyclohexane Dissolve 5 g of adipoyl chloride in 95 mL of cyclohexane.	125 mL
20% Sodium hydroxide solution Dissolve 10 g of sodium hydroxide in 40 mL of water and place it in a plastic bottle.	10 mL
6 inch lengths of copper wire	10 pieces

<u>PROCEDURE 55C</u>

It is recommended that this experiment be performed as a demonstration since the glass-ware is difficult to clean. We prepare a large batch <u>in a hood</u> in a container, and reuse this container each time the experiment is performed. The surface of the hood should be covered with butcher paper or newspaper.

Styrene   300 mL
    Styrene thinner is available in gallon
    quantities at greatly reduced cost from
    commercial suppliers of polyester resins.
    One supplier is: Titan Chemicals, Inc.,
    Seattle, Washington and Santa Ana,
    California.

Benzoyl peroxide   7 g

2 liter Erlenmeyer flask (reusable)

Hot plate

Newspaper or butcher paper

Stirring rod

<u>PROCEDURE 55D</u>

Mixture A   225 mL
    Prepared as follows: Place 350 g of
    castor oil, 100 g of glycerol, 50 drops
    of stannous octoate (stannous 2-ethylhex-
    anoate), 50 drops of Dow-Corning 200 sili-
    cone oil viscosity of 350 cs or less (this
    is estimated since it is difficult to mea-
    sure), and 150 drops of water in a bottle.
    Cap the bottle and shake it thoroughly.
    Allow this mixture to stand no more than 12
    hours before use.

    The silicone oil is available from Varian As-
    soc. (82-001520-00) and FOXBORO ANALABS (SGP-
    197); Stannous 2-ethylhexanoate is supplied by
    Sigma Chemical Co.; castor oil is available
    from EM Science (CX0545).

Toluene-2,4-diisocyanate (TDI)   125 mL
    This must be placed in a hood. See
    warning on page 420 of the Text.

1 pt. waxed soft drink cups   10 cups

25 mL Graduated cylinders   2 cylinders
    Place these by the TDI and mixture
    A to dispense the viscous and <u>messy</u>
    liquids.

ANSWERS TO QUESTIONS:

1. $-CH_2-CH_2-S-S-S-S-CH_2CH_2-S-S-S-S-$

2.

$$\left(CH_2-\underset{\underset{Cl}{|}}{\overset{\overset{Cl}{|}}{C}}-CH_2-\underset{}{\overset{\overset{Cl}{|}}{CH}}\right)_n$$

3.

$$-CH_2-\underset{\underset{CH_3}{|}}{\overset{\overset{CH_3}{|}}{C}}-CH_2-\underset{\underset{CH_3}{|}}{\overset{\overset{CH_3}{|}}{C}}-$$

4.

$$\underset{F}{\overset{F}{}}C = C\underset{Cl}{\overset{F}{}}$$

5.

$$-O-CH_2-CH_2-O-\underset{\underset{O}{\|}}{C}\overset{H\quad H}{=}\underset{\underset{O}{\|}}{C}-O-CH_2CH_2-O-\underset{\underset{O}{\|}}{C}\overset{H\quad H}{=}\underset{\underset{O}{\|}}{C}-O-CH_2CH_2-O-$$

6.

$$-OCH_2-\bigcirc-CH_2O-\overset{\overset{O}{\|}}{C}-\bigcirc-\overset{\overset{O}{\|}}{C}-OCH_2-\bigcirc-CH_2-O-$$

Experiment 56

IDENTIFICATION OF UNKNOWNS

TIME ESTIMATE: Extremely variable, depending on how the
   experiment is utilized.

   In our course, we schedule this experiment in the second
quarter (or semester) of the laboratory and expect students to
complete it on top of all other experiments during the quarter. Normally we assign one period at the very beginning to
this lab. During this period and subsequent ones, the stud-
dents are expected to try all the tests on known compounds and

record the results. Once this has been completed, two unknowns (a solid and a liquid) are issued and students are expected to work on these in whatever free time they may have during the quarter (i.e., while waiting for a reflux period). Finally, we usually leave one or more unscheduled periods free at the end of the lab schedule to allow students to complete unfinished details of their unknowns. Extra credit unknowns may also be attempted.

We also generally require students to classify a series of five solubility unknowns (weak acid, strong acid, base, neutral-no functionality, neutral-with functionality) and, in some cases, we use a set of elemental unknowns (e.g., Cl, N, S, N+Cl, I) which must also be classified. However, we generally discourage the use of sodium fusion tests except where absolutely necessary.

Some instructors may prefer to issue spectra at the same time as the unknowns are issued. We prefer that the student not bypass learning the chemical tests, and only issue spectra (students determine their own IR spectra) once the student has achieved a preliminary chemical identification of the functional group. Either approach is possible.

We prefer to issue general unknowns (functional group unknown). However, some instructors may wish to issue group or class unknowns (functional group known). We have tried to sectionalize the experiment in such a way that either approach is possible. Thus, for instance, it should also be possible to issue an unknown amine, an unknown aldehyde/ketone, etc.

In choosing our lists of unknowns, we have considered both cost and general availability. Most of the unknowns listed are common to most stockrooms and (at least at the time of writing) generally cost less than $15 per 100 g.

To assist students in acquiring all available literature data, we supply in the lab a copy of each of the following reference works and encourage their use:

1.   Handbook of Chemistry and Physics

2.   Tables for the Identification of Organic Compounds

3.   The Merck Index

159

4.   Shriner, Fuson, Curtin, and Morrill

5.   Pasto and Johnson

These books are permanently mounted, either on a stand or a chained board, to prevent their removal from the lab. We encourage students to use these supplementary texts and references. Additionally, we sometimes issue extra unknowns (beyond the first liquid and first solid) which may or may not be listed in the tables of our own book. For some of the better students, we may not even stick to the functional groups covered in our text.

We maintain a special set of shelves in our laboratory where all the test reagents, test compounds, and special solvents are collected. This is convenient and save a lot of confusion.

A computer simulation of this lab by D. Pavia, "Simulated Qualitative Organic Analysis - SQUALOR," is available from COMPress (IBM PC, CGA Card, 256K). Forthcoming data disks for the "IR and NMR Simulator" programs by Paul Schatz (COMPress) should contain spectra for all of the unknowns listed in Appendix 1. Schools without these instruments will be able to make optimum use of this experiment.

TEST SOLUTIONS AND REAGENTS

PROCEDURE 56A

SOLUBILITY TESTS

REAGENTS: UNKNOWNS:

Concentrated H_2SO_4 1. Dimethylaniline
                                          (strong base)

5% aqueous HCl   2. 2-Naphthol
                                          (weak acid)

5% aqueous $NaHCO_3$ 3. Benzoic acid
                                          (strong acid)

5% aqueous NaOH   4. Benzophenone (neu-
                                          tral-functionality)

Organic solvents: 5. Biphenyl (neutral-
    ether, hexane   no functionality)
    CH_2Cl_2, acetone   —of course other are
                                          possible

ELEMENTAL TESTS

Copper wire

2% Ethanolic $AgNO_3$
(2 g/100 mL)

5% Nitric acid

15% NaI in acetone
(15 g/100 mL)

2 M Potassium hydroxide in
methanol

5% Aqueous ferrous ammonium
sulfate (5 g/100 mL)

3 N Sulfuric acid

SODIUM FUSION:

Sodium metal (stored under mineral oil) We
usually place this in a designated hood,
along with a triple beam balance, a knife, a
shallow dish, and a waste container.

Methanol

pH paper

Sat'd ferrous ammonium
sulfate (5 g/100 mL)

30% Aqueous KF (30 g/100 mL
H_2O)

Acetic acid (conc.)

1% Aqueous lead acetate
(1 g/100 mL)

5% Aqueous $AgNO_3$
(5 g/100 mL)

TEST COMPOUNDS:

Bromobenzene

Benzoic acid

Benzyl bromide
(α-Bromotoluene)

10% Aqueous H_2SO_4

Chlorine water or cal-
cium hypochlorite
(Chlorox may also be
used)

10% Aqueous NaOH

UNKNOWNS (if desired)

Your choice - N, S,
Cl, Br, I, or combina-
tions

Methylene chloride

<u>PROCEDURE 56C</u>

TESTS FOR UNSATURATION   TEST COMPOUNDS:

Carbon tetrachloride or   Cyclohexene
    Methylene chloride*
                                          Cyclohexane
2% Br_2/CCl_4 (2 mL/98 mL*)
                                          Acetone
1,2-Dimethoxyethane
                                          Toluene
95% Ethanol
                                          Naphthalene
1% Aqueous $KMnO_4$ (1 g/100 mL)

* Methylene chloride may be used in place of carbon
tetrachloride, however, see section 56C of the Text for a
discussion of problems with this substitution.

<u>PROCEDURE 56D</u>

ALDEHYDES AND KETONES   TEST COMPOUNDS:

2,4-Dinitrophenylhydra-   Cyclohexanone
    zine agent:
                                          Benzaldehyde
    Dissolve 3.0 g of 2,4-
dinitropheylhydrazine in 15   Benzophenone
mL conc. H_2SO_4. In a beaker,
mix together 20 mL H_2O and 70   Butanol (butyralde-
mL 95% ethanol. With vigorous   hyde)
stirring, slowly add the 2,4-
dinitrophenylhydrazine solution to the aqueous ethanol
mixture. After thorough mixing,
filter the solution by gravity
through a fluted filter. Be
sure to test the solution on a
known compound.

95% Ethanol

Bis(2-ethoxyethyl) ether

162

Reagent grade acetone

Chromic acid reagent:

Dissolve 1.0 g Chromium tri-
oxide (CrO_3) in 1 mL conc. H_2SO_4.
Add carefully to 3 mL H_2O. (Scale
about 20 times for a stock bottle.)

Tollen's Reagent

Solution A: 3 g $AgNO_3$ in 30 mL H_2O

Solution B: 10% aqueous NaOH

Bis(2-ethoxyethyl) ether

Iodoform Reagent

Dissolve 20 g KI and 10 g I_2 in
100 mL H_2O

Bis(2-ethoxyethyl) ether

2.5% Aqueous ferric chloride (2.5 g/100 mL)

FOR DERIVATIVE PREPARATION:

2 M aqueous solution of semicarbazide
    hydrochloride (1.1 g for every 5
    mL H_2O)

Semicarbazide hydrochloride

Sodium acetate

Ethanol

2,4-Dinitrophenylhydrazine reagent
    (as prepared above)

PROCEDURE 56E

CARBOXYLIC ACIDS   TEST COMPOUNDS:

2% ethanolic $AgNO_3$ (2 g/100 mL)   Benzoic acid

Phenophthalein indicator

163

Standardized NaOH solution
(approx. 0.1 N)

10% aqueous sodium carbonate

FOR DERIVATIVE PREPARATION:

Thionyl chloride	Anhydrous Na_2SO_4
Conc. NH_4OH	5% Aqueous NaOH
Aniline	5% Aqueous HCl
p-Toluidine	
Toluene	

PROCEDURE 56F

PHENOLS   TEST COMPOUNDS:

2.5% Aqueous ferric   Phenol
   chloride (2.5 g/100 mL)

Methylene chloride

Pyridine

1% $FeCl_3$/$CHCl_3$ (1 g/100 mL)

Saturated bromine water:
   Add bromine to water until
   it no longer dissolves and
   forms a red pool in the bottom - use a glass stoppered
   bottle.

FOR DERIVATIVE PREPARATION:

α-Naphthylisocyanate   Methanol

Brominating solution:
   0.5 g Br_2 and 0.75 g

   KBr for each 5 mL H_2O

PROCEDURE 56G

164

AMINES

10% Sodium hydroxide

10% Potassium hydroxide

p-Toluenesulfonyl chloride

Benzenesulfonyl chloride

10% Sodium nitrite solution

2-Naphthol (β-naphthol)

Acetyl chloride

pH paper

Waste container for nitrous
    acid test

TEST COMPOUNDS:

Aniline

N-Methylaniline

N,N-Dimethylaniline

Butylamine

Pyridine

FOR DERIVATIVE PREPARATION:

Acetic anhydride

5% Aqueous HCl

Pyridine

5% Aqueous H_2SO_4

10% Aqueous NaOH

Benzoyl chloride

Ethanol

5% Aqueous Na_2CO_3

Toluene

Sat'd picric acid in
    EtOH

Methyl iodide

Ethyl acetate

PROCEDURE 56H

ALCOHOLS

Acetyl chloride

Lucas Reagent:

    Cool 10 mL of conc. HCl

TEST COMPOUNDS:

1-Butanol (n-butyl
    alcohol)

2-Butanol (sec-butyl
    alcohol)

in a beaker using an ice bath. While still cooling, and, with stirring, add 16 g anhydrous zinc chloride to the acid.

2-Methyl-2-propanol (t-butyl alcohol)

Chromic acid Reagent
(See Procedure 56D)

FOR DERIVATIVE PREPARATION:

3,5-Dinitrobenzoyl chloride

Check purity as indicated on page 693, 694.

5% Aqueous Na_2CO_3

Phenylisocyanate

Ethanol

Ligroin or hexane

PROCEDURE 56I

ESTERS

Hydroxylamine hydrochloride
(0.5 N in ethanol)

5% Aqueous $FeCl_3$ (5 g/100 mL)

1N Aqueous HCl

6N Aqueous NaOH

95% Ethanol

Experiment 57

CARBOHYDRATES

TIME ESTIMATE: 2 periods, including all tests and an unknown.

Galactose and lactose can be determined as an unknown

without the mucic acid test by employing the remaining tests. If the mucic acid test is to be run, it should be started earlier in the laboratory period since it requires a 1 hour heating period (Exp. 58). The carbohydrate solutions and reagents should be placed in several different locations in the laboratory depending on the number of students. Bottles should be supplied with droppers. Students should be instructed on methods of estimating volumes to help them save time (calibrated droppers, counting drops, marked test tubes, etc.). Weights of solids may be estimated by volume measurement.

CHEMICALS PER 10 STUDENTS:

Xylose, arabinose, glucose, galactose, fructose, sucrose, starch, glycogen (Glycogen from oysters, Sigma Chemical Co., No. G-8751)	10 g each
Lactose	12 g

The above amounts of carbohydrates include enough material to make all of the 1% solutions, provide solids for the mucic acid and osazone tests, and provide unknowns.

Place the following 1% carbohydrate solutions and test reagents in several locations in the laboratory depending upon the numbers of students. Equip each container with a dropper.

1%	Carbohydrate solutions (1g/100 mL distilled water (xylose, arabinose, glucose, galactose, fructose, lactose, starch, glycogen	150 mL
1%	Sucrose solution (1 g/100 mL distilled water)	175 mL
	Molisch Test Reagent Dissolve 5 g of α-naphthol in 100 mL of 95% ethanol. (enough reagent for 75 students).	15 mL
	Sulfuric acid	650 mL
	Bial's Test Reagent	375 mL

167

Dissolve 3 g of orcinol (Sigma Chemical Co., No. 0-1875) in 1 liter of conc. hydrochloric acid and add 3 mL of 10% aqueous ferric chloride. (enough reagent for 25 students)

1-Pentanol (n-amyl alcohol)   125 mL

Seliwanoff's Test Reagent   500 mL
Dissolve 0.5 g of resorcinol in 1 liter of dilute hydrochloric acid (1 volume of conc. hydrochloric acid and 2 volumes of distilled water). (20 students)

Benedict's Test Reagent   625 mL
Dissolve 173 g of hydrated sodium citrate and 100 g of anhydrous sodium carbonate in 800 mL of distilled water, with heating. Filter the solution. Add to it a solution of 17.3 g of cupric sulfate ($CuSO_4 \cdot 5\ H_2O$) dissolved in 100 mL of distilled water. Dilute the combined solutions to 1 liter. (enough reagent for 15 students)

Barfoed's Test Reagent   625 mL

Dissolve 66.6 g of cupric acetate in 1 liter of distilled water. Filter the solution, if necessary, and add 9 mL of glacial acetic acid. (enough reagent for 15 students)

Phenylhydrazine Reagent (osazone formation)   575 mL
Dissolve 50 g of phenylhydrazine hydrochloride and 75 g of sodium acetate trihydrate in 500 mL of distilled water. The reagent is somewhat unstable. (enough reagent for about 10 students)

Starch-iodine Test Solution   2 mL
Dissolve 2 g of potassium iodide in 50 mL of distilled water. Add 1 g of iodine and shake the solution until the iodine dissolves. Dilute the solution to 100 mL.

168

Sodium Thiosulfate Solution	4 mL
Dissolve 2.5 g of sodium thiosulfate in 100 mL of water.	
Conc. hydrochloric acid	4 mL
10% Sodium hydroxide solution	25 mL
Conc. nitric acid	75 mL

Containers of carbohydrates should be placed in the laboratory for the osazone formation experiment and mucic acid test.

Xylose, arbinose, fructose, sucrose, starch glycogen	2 g
Glucose, galactose	3 g
Lactose	4 g

Unknowns

    0.4 and 0.5 g samples of unknown carbohy-drates should be issued to the students. Starch is a poor unknown because it is insoluble in water, and it is easy to identify.

RESULTS:

	Substance	Molisch	Bial's	Benedict's	Barfoed's
1	Control	no color	no color	no ppt.	no ppt.
2	xylose	purple	blue-green	red ppt.	red ppt.
3	arabinose	purple	blue-green	red ppt.	red ppt.
4	glucose	purple	brown (amyl Alc)	red ppt.	red ppt.
5	galactose	purple	green (amyl Alc)	red ppt.	red ppt.
6	fructose	brownish purple	red-brown	red ppt.	red ppt.
7	lactose	purple	slight brown (amyl Alc)	brown ppt.	no ppt.
8	sucrose	brownish purple	red-brown	no ppt.	no ppt.
9	starch	purple	brown (amyl Alc)	no ppt.	no ppt.
10	glycogen	purple	brown (amyl Alc)	no ppt.	no ppt.

Seliwanoff's test: NC = no color; VS = very slight; LT = light; DK = dark

	1	2	3	4	5	6	7	8	9	10
1 min	NC	NC	NC	NC	NC	DK RED	NC	LT RED	NC	NC
2 min	NC	NC	NC	NC	NC	DK RED	NC	LT RED	NC	NC
3 min	NC	NC	NC	NC	NC	DK RED	NC	LT RED	NC	NC
4 min	NC	NC	NC	NC	NC	DK RED	NC	DK RED	NC	NC
5 min	NC	NC	NC	VS RED	NC	DK RED	NC	DK RED	NC	NC
6 min	NC	NC	NC	VS RED	VS RED	DK RED	VS RED	DK RED	VS RED	VS RED

Osazone formation (Procedure C)

	Time (min)	Observations
2 xylose	9	turned from clear yellow to murky yellow, fine precip. (non-crystalline)
3 arabinose	15	turned from clear yellow to murky yellow, fine precip. (non-crystalline)
4 glucose	8	yellow precip. (crystalline)
5 galactose	24	very slowly begins to turn murky yellow, fine precip. (non-crystalline)
6 fructose	2	yellow precip. (crystalline)
7 lactose	--	remained clear yellow for 30 min., precip. after 5 min at room temperature, (crystalline)
8 sucrose	20	changes from clear and colorless solution to yellow after 15 min., then deposits crystalline precip.
9 starch	--	remained clear and colorless for 30 min.
10 glycogen	--	remained clear and colorless for 30 min.

Notes: fructose and glucose - easy to see when crystals start forming.
xylose and arabinose - hard to see when precipitation starts.

Iodine test for starch (Procedure D)
Purple color with starch, only. Decolorized with sodium thio-
sulfate solution.

Hydrolysis of sucrose (Procedure E)
Red precipitate with Benedict's reagent.

Mucic acid test (Procedure F)
Precipitate forms with lactose and galactose, no precipitate from
glucose.

ANSWERS TO QUESTIONS:
1.

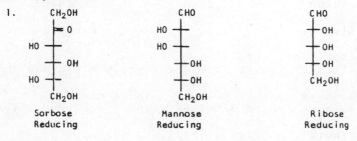

Sorbose
Reducing

Mannose
Reducing

Ribose
Reducing

Maltose:

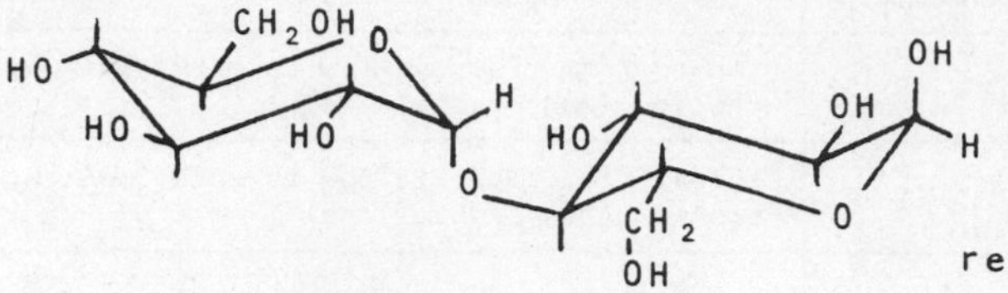

reducing

Raffinose: Trisaccharide made up of fructose, galactose, and glucose moieties. Non-reducing.

Cellulose:

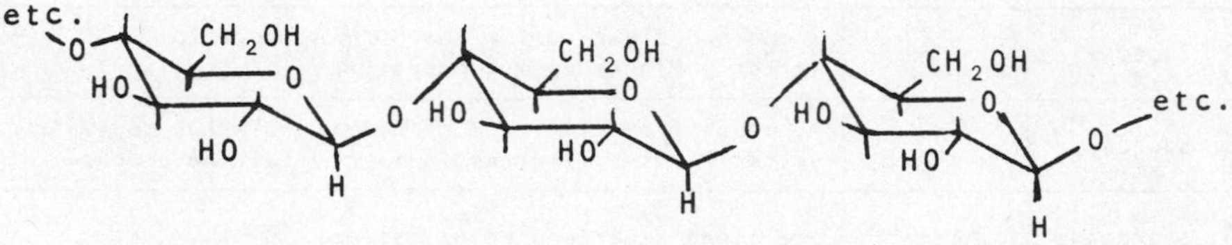

non-reducing

2. Mannose differs from glucose only at C-2. The chiral center is destroyed upon oxidation with phenylhydrazine. The dihydrazone (osozone) thus formed is identical from both sugars.

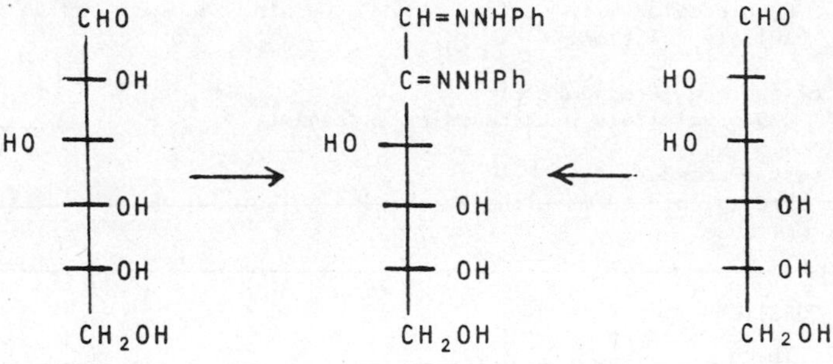

Glucose   Mannose

3. Molisch: all purple
    Bial's: ribose is blue-green, rest are brown
    Seliwanoff's:
        sorbose- dark red after 1 and 6 min.
        mannose- no color after 1 and slight red after
                6 min.
        ribose- no color after 1 and 6 min.
        maltose- no color after 1 and slight red after
                6 min.

172

raffinose- lt. red after 1 and dark red after
6 min.
cellulose- no color after 1 and slight red
after 6 min.
Barfoed's: Sorbose, mannose, ribose form precipitates, others do not form precipitates.
Mucic acid test: Raffinose gives a precipitate,
the others do not.

4.

Fructose   Glucose

5.

6.

$R =$

Experiment 58

ISOLATION OF CASEIN AND
LACTOSE FROM MILK

TIME ESTIMATE: 1 period. The collection of the lactose crystals requires about one-half hour during the following laboratory period. If both of the optional tests are completed, an additional hour is required.

CHEMICALS PER 10 STUDENTS:

Fresh non-fat (skim) milk   1/2 gallon
     The milk should not be allowed to
stand too long before being used in this
experiment. Lactose may be slowly converted to lactic acid even if it is
stored in a refrigerator. Powdered milk
may be mixed and used in lieu of fresh
milk.

Dilute acetic acid   500 mL
     Add 1 volume of glacial acetic acid
to 10 volumes of water

Powdered calcium carbonate   65 g

Applicator sticks   50

95% Ethanol   2.5 L

Decolorizing carbon (Norit)   25 g

Filter Aid (Celite)   25 g

Benedict's reagent (optional test)   200 mL
     See Instructor's Manual, Exp. 57

1% Glucose solution (1 g/100 mL   15 mL
     distilled water)

1% Galactose solution (1 g/100 mL   15 mL
     distilled water)

Mucic acid test (optional test)

Glucose (dextrose)   2 g

Galactose	2 g
Conc. nitric acid	75 mL
Hot plates	

ANSWERS TO QUESTIONS:

1. A rotation of zero should be obtained. Mucic acid has a plane of symmetry, and it optically inactive.

2.

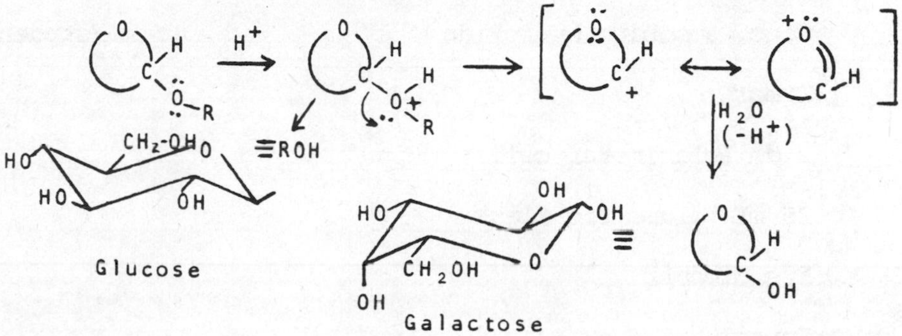

3. β-Lactose has all of the groups equatorial on the glucose moiety, while α-lactose has an axial group (see page 485). Thus, β-lactose is the thermodynamically more stable of the two isomers.

4. Even though there is only a small amount of free aldehyde form present at any given time, it is immediately oxidized by Benedict's reagent. The equilibrium shifts to produce more of the aldehyde form, and that in turn is oxidized. The process is repeated countless numbers of times, until the lactose is completely oxidized.

5.

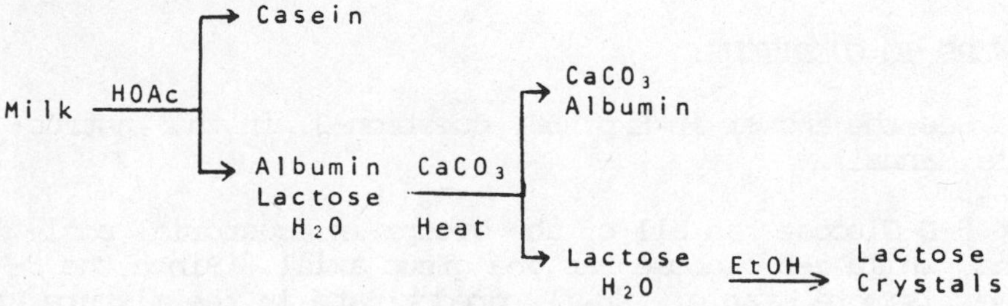

MUTAROTATION OF LACTOSE

TIME ESTIMATE: About 1 hour. This experiment must be co-scheduled with other experiments over several laboratory periods unless a number of polarimeters are available.

CHEMICALS, SUPPLIES AND EQUIPMENT:

α-Lactose   1.25 g/student
      The material from Exp. 58 may
      be used.

Conc. ammonium hydroxide   0.5 mL/student

Timer

2 dm Polarimeter cell

25 mL Volumetric flask

Eye dropper

Funnel

Thermometer

Graph paper

French curve

Polarimeter
      The Zeiss polarimeter is described in this experi-
      ment and Technique 15. The amounts and concentra-
      tions may have to be altered if other instruments
      and/or cells are used.

ANSWERS TO QUESTIONS:

1.   See the answer in Exp. 58, question 3, in the Instructor's Manual.

2.   β-D-Glucose has all of the groups in equatorial positions, while α-D-glucose has one group axial. Since the β-
isomer is more stable, it will predominate in the mixture at

equilibrium.

$$\frac{52.7 - 18.7}{112.2 - 18.7} \times 100 = 36.3\% \; \alpha; \; 63.7\% \; \beta$$

Experiment 60

PAPER CHROMATOGRAPHY OF AMINO ACIDS

TIME ESTIMATE: 1 period, with the protein hydrolysates
   supplied by the laboratory instructor. It is suggested
   that the four hydrolysates be supplied in order to save
   time. The experiment should be started early in the
   laboratory period because of the four-hour development
   time for the paper chromatography. The chromatograms may
   have to be removed by the instructor or assistant. During
   the following period, enough time will have to be allowed
   for visualizing the amino acids with ninhydrin spray.

CHEMICALS AND SUPPLIES:

   Hydrolysates (four total, preferably supplied by the
      laboratory instructor). The procedure for the
      preparation of the hydrolysates is given on page
      494. The procedure provides enough of the hydroly-
      sates for about 15 students.

   19% Hydrochloric acid solution   100 mL
        Equal volumes of conc. hydrochloric
        acid and distilled water

   Casein (Calbiochem Co., #21855 or Exp. 58)   0.5 g

   Gelatin (J.T. Baker Co.)   0.5 g

   Hair (local barber shop; use men's hair)   0.5 g

   Silk (available from a fabric store, Coats   0.5 g
      and Clark's, silk twist thread, #256,
      size D, about 1/2 of a 10 yd. spool

   Decolorizing carbon (Norit)   0.5 g

      Place 10 mL portions of the hydrolysates in
      labeled cork stoppered bottles. Embed a

177

micropipet in each cork. Write the name of
the cork and label. Save some of the hydrolysates for parts VI and VII of optional procedures in the Instructor's Manual.

0.1 M Amino acid standards (9 total)   10 mL
                                                        each

Aspartic acid (Mol. wt. 133.1), alanine
(Mol. wt. 89.1), glycine (Mol. wt. 75.1),
tyrosine (Mol. wt. 181.2), proline (Mol.
wt. 115.1), leucine (Mol. wt. 131.2),
glutamic acid (Mol. wt. 147.1), cystine
(Mol. wt. 240.3), arginine (Mol. wt. 210.7).
Acidify each of the 10 mL samples with 10
drops of 19% HCl. Each 10 mL standard solution will supply over 100 students. All of
the amino acids are available from Sigma Chem.
Co.

Place the standards in labeled bottles, equipped with micropipets. The micropipets can be
embedded in the cork stopper. Write the abbre-
viation for the amino acids on the cork and label.

Unknowns (5 total)   10 mL
                                                        each

The best unknowns (easy to identify) are:
acidified 0.1 M solutions of aspartic acid,
cystine, glutamic acid, proline and tyrosine.

Place the unknowns in containers, equipped
with micropipets as indicated above, and
number them 1 through 5. The students apply
the unknowns to the chromatrogram along with
the standards and two hydrolysates. Proline
yields a yellow spot with ninhydrin, tyrosine
give a gray spot, the remaining amino acids
give deep blue spots.

Paper Chromatography

Whatman #1 paper (57 x 46 cm sheet) cut

178

into 6-24 x 15.5 cm rectangles as follows:

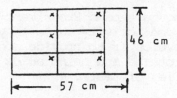

The Whatman #1 paper is supplied in packages
of 100 sheets each. They must be handled carefully to avoid finger prints. The "x" is placed in the corner on each piece as indicated,
using a pencil, not a pen. Cut the remaining
piece of paper into smaller sections for students
to use in practicing their spotting technique.

Capillary tubing for preparing micropipets
It is suggested that the micropipets be supplied
by the instructor with the amino acid standards,
hydrolysates and unknowns (18 needed).

Scissors

32 oz. wide-mouth screw cap jar (1/student)

80% Aqueous phenol (20 mL/student)
The solution is prepared by mixing 80 g of phenol
per 20 mL of distilled water. Heat the mixture until
it dissolves completely. Add a protective layer of
ligroin so that air is excluded from the aqueous
phenol. If the ligroin is not added, the solution
should be used as soon as possible. Place the
solution in a large Erlenmeyer flask. A 10 mL pipet
and bulb should be available for transferring the
phenol.

Paper clips (1/student)

Ninhydrin spray
Available in an aerosol can: Gelman Instrument Co.,
#72818, available from chemical suppliers.

Oven adjusted to 110°

Rulers (millimeter)

OPTIONAL TESTS ON PROTEIN AND AMINO ACIDS

Instructors wishing to expand Experiment 60, in order to provide students with some activity while they are waiting for the chromatograms to develop or to provide additional laboratory experience with proteins and amino acids may wish to consider the following series of tests.

I.   Amphoteric Properties of Proteins

Amino acids can function as acids or bases by forming salts with strong acids and bases. Compounds which have such behavior are said to be amphoteric.

$$RCH-COO^-Na^+ \xleftarrow{\ NaOH\ } \underset{+NH_3}{RCH-COO^-} \xrightarrow{\ HCl\ } \underset{+NH_3}{R-CH-COOH}$$

Dipolar Structure
of Amino Acid

Proteins can also have amphoteric behavior and may dissolve to some extent in an acidic or basic solution. This results from the fact that some amino acid components of the protein have free amino groups (lysine and arginine) and free carboxyl groups (aspartic and glutamic acids). These groups may react with acids or bases to form soluble salts of a protein.

$$-N-CH-C-N-CH-C-$$

Aspartic Acid / Lysine structure

Aspartic Acid   Lysine

A.   Place 0.1 g of casein in a test tube and add to it 5 mL of water and 2 mL of 10% sodium hydroxide solution. Stopper the test tube, shake it vigorously and observe the result.

180

Save 2 mL of this mixture for use in part VI.

B.   Add concentrated hydrochloric acid dropwise, with shaking, to the remaining solution from Part A and observe the result.   Continue until 4 mL of the acid have have been added, stopper the test tube, shake it vigorously and observe the result.

II. Coagulation of Proteins

The α-helix structure of a protein is maintained by hydrogen bonds between the amino acid in one part of the protein with another amino acid in another part. The stable nature of such a protein can be disturbed by physical and chemical means by breaking the hydrogen bonds. The α-helix may then unfold and precipitate. Such a protein is said to be <u>denatured</u>. Proteins can be precipitated (coagulated) with heat, strong acids, or with alcohol.

A.   Place about 2 mL of egg albumin solution in a test tube and boil it gently for a few minutes. Observe what happens to the heated solution.

B.   Place about 2 mL of an egg albumin solution in a test tube and add 7 mL of 95% ethanol. Observe what happens to the solution.

III. Precipitation of Heavy Metal Ions

Heavy metal ions, such as silver, lead, and mercury, precipitate proteins by combination of a metal cation with the free carboxylate groups of the protein. The antiseptic action of silver nitrate and mercuric chloride depends upon the precipitation of the proteins present in bacteria.

$$\text{protein} - \underset{\underset{O}{\|}}{C}O^- + Ag^+ \longrightarrow \text{protein} - \underset{\underset{O}{\|}}{C}O^- Ag^+$$

Silver Precipitate

A.   Place about 2 mL of egg albumin solution in a test tube and add 2% silver nitrate dropwise. Observe what happens to the solution.

B.   Repeat the above with 5% mercuric chloride solution.

181

IV. Xanthoproteic Test

Some amino acids incorporated into a protein have aromatic rings. These rings undergo nitration to give yellow compounds. In basic solution the color intensifies.

Place 2 mL of egg albumin solution in a test tube and add 10 drops of concentrated nitric acid. Gently warm the mixture and observe any change in color. Cool the mixture and add 10% sodium hydroxide solution dropwise until the solution is basic. Note any change in color.

V. Sulfur Test

Proteins which have sulfur-containing amino acids, such as cystine (disulfide bond), are cleaved in basic solution to give an inorganic sulfide. In the presence of lead acetate, a black precipitate of lead sulfide is produced.

$$\text{Sulfur-containing protein} \xrightarrow{\text{NaOH}} S^= \xrightarrow{Pb^{++}} PbS$$

Black Precipitate

Add 2 mL of egg albumin solution, 5 mL of 10% sodium hydroxide solution, and 2 drops of 5% lead acetate solution to a small Erlenmeyer flask. Carefully boil (froth) the mixture, with mixing, for a few minutes and observe the result.

VI. Biuret Test

When urea is heated above its melting point, it is converted to biuret with liberation of ammonia,

Biuret forms a pink or violet colored complex with cupric ion

182

in basic solution. When the pink-violet color is obtained, the test is said to be positive. A positive biuret test is also obtained with all compounds which contain two or more peptide bonds (tripeptide or large peptide). Amino acids (except serine and threonine), dipeptides, and urea do not give violet colors with cupric ion and are said to give negative tests. Amino acids, in a similar fashion to ammonia, produce a blue solution in the presence of cupric ion. The test is quite useful in following the hydrolysis of proteins in order to determine when the hydrolysis reaction is completed.

A.   Place 1 g of urea in a dry test tube. Gently heat the test tube until the urea melts. Cautiously note the odor of the gas which evolves and test it with a piece of moist red litmus paper held over the mouth of the test tube. Gently continue to heat the mixture until the material appears to be solidifying. Dissolve the white residue in 5 mL of warm water and filter the mixture. Add 4 mL of 10% sodium hydroxide solution to the filtrate, with mixing. Add 10 drops of a 2% copper sulfate solution. Shake the mixture and observe the color.

B.   Place 2 mL of egg albumin solution in a test tube and add 2 mL of 10% sodium hydroxide. Add 5 drops of 2% copper sulfate solution and shake the mixture. Observe the color of the solution.

C.   Add 2 mL of water and 2 drops of 2% copper sulfate solution to the 2 mL of casein solution from part IA. Shake the mixture and observe the color.

D.   Place 0.1 g of glycine in a test tube and add 3 mL of 10% sodium hydroxide solution to dissolve the solid. Add 10 drops of 2% copper sulfate solution, shake the mixture and observe the color.

E.   Place 5 drops of hydrolysate from Experiment 60 and 10 drops of 10% sodium hydroxide solution in a test tube. Check the solution with litmus paper to make sure that it is definitely alkaline. Add more 10% sodium hydroxide solution if necessary. Add 4 or 5 drops of 2% copper sulfate solution. A blue color indicates that the hydrolysis is complete. A pink or violet color indicates that the hydrolysis is not complete.

VII. Nitrous Acid Test

Amino acids react with nitrous acid to give an α-hydroxy acid

183

and <u>nitrogen gas</u>.

$$R-CH-COOH + HONO \longrightarrow RCH-COOH + H_2O + N_2$$
$$| |$$
$$NH_2 OH$$

Since most amino groups in a protein are involved in peptide bonds, they are available for this reaction. Proteins, however, do contain some free amino groups, mostly from the amino acid lysine. These free amino groups react with nitrous acid to produce nitrogen gas. However, they do not liberate as much nitrogen as the amino acids themselves.

Conduct each of the tests at approximately the same time.

A.   Place 0.1 g of glycine in a test tube and add 5 mL of 10% hydrochloric acid. Carefully add 1 mL of 5% sodium nitrite solution to the test tube. Shake it well and observe the rate of gas evolution.

B.   Place 4 or 5 grains of gelatin in a test tube and add 3 drops of 19% hydrochloric acid. Add 3 drops of 5% sodium nitrite solution to the mixture. Shake it well and observe the rate of evolution of gas.

C.   Place about 10 drops of hydrolysate from Experiment 60 in a test tube and add about 20 drops of 5% sodium nitrite solution. Shake the mixture well and observe the rate of gas evolution.

CHEMICALS AND SUPPLIES PER 10 STUDENTS:

The following chemicals and solutions should not be placed in the same location as the paper chromatography supplies.

Casein (Calbiochem Co., #21855 or Exp. 58)   2 g

Albumin (egg)   175 mL
    Prepared by adding 4 g of dried albumin
    (J.T. Baker Co., and others) to 200 mL
    of distilled water. Allow the mixture
    to stand overnight. Gravity filter the
    resulting mixture. A graduated pipet
    should be available for transferring the
    solution.

Gelatin (J.T. Baker Co.)	1 g
Glycine	3 g
Urea	15 g

Place the following solutions in bottles equipped with droppers.

10% sodium hydroxide solution	225 mL
Conc. hydrochloric acid	50 mL
95% Ethanol	100 mL

2% Silver nitrate solution
    2 g silver nitrate per 100 mL distilled
    water
	5 mL

5% Mercuric chloride solution
    5 g mercuric chloride per 100 mL distilled
    water
	5 mL

Conc. nitric acid	10 mL

5% Lead acetate solution
    5 g lead acetate per 100 mL distilled
    water
	5 mL

2% Copper sulfate solution 2 g anhyd. cupric sulfate per 100 mL water	25 mL
10% Hydrochloric acid solution	75 mL

5% Sodium nitrite solution
    5 g sodium nitrite per 100 mL distilled
    water
	30 mL

19% Hydrochloric acid solution
    Equal volumes of conc. hydrochloric acid
    and distilled water
	5 mL

4 Hydrolysates (from Experiment 60)	5 mL each

RESOLUTION OF
(+/−)−α−PHENYLETHYLAMINE

TIME ESTIMATE: 1 period. It is recommended that the tartaric acid, amine, and methanol be prepared two laboratory periods before the remainder of the experiment is completed. If this is done, the solutions can be reheated if poor crystals are formed. See the first paragraph on page 497.

CHEMICALS AND SUPPLIES PER 10 STUDENTS:

L−(+)−Tartaric acid	400 g
Methanol	6 L
(+/−)−α−Phenylethylamine (α−methylbenzylamine or 1−phenylethylamine)	350 g
50% Sodium hydroxide solution Prepared by dissolving 250 g of sodium hydroxide in 250 mL of water. This gives about 340 mL of 50% NaOH.	200 mL
Diethyl ether	1.5 L
Anhydrous magnesium sulfate	25 g
1 L Erlenmeyer flask	10

SPECIAL EQUIPMENT:

Polarimeter
   The Zeiss polarimeter is described in
   Technique 15.

2 dm Polarimeter cell (or a 0.5 dm cell − see
   footnote on p. 498)

10 mL pipet

ANSWERS TO QUESTIONS:

1. Reagents used to resolve acidic compounds:

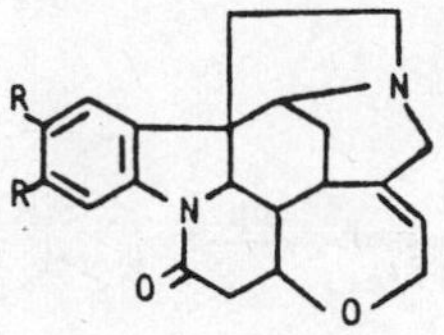

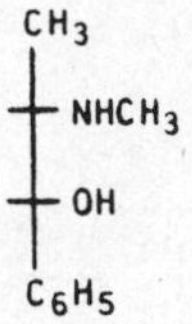

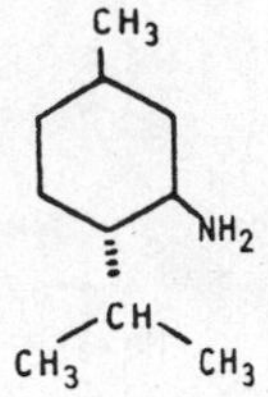

R = H (-)-Strychnine   (-)-Ephedrine   Menthylamine
R = OCH$_3$ (-)-Brucine

Reagents used to resolve basic compounds:

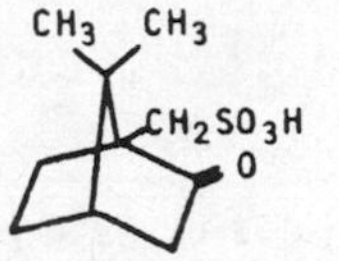

(+)-Camphor-10-sulfonic   (-)-Menthoxyacetic   (+)-Tartaric acid 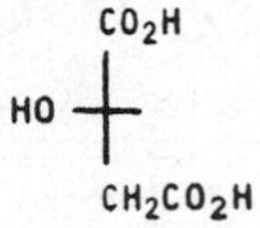   (-)-Malic acid
        acid   acid

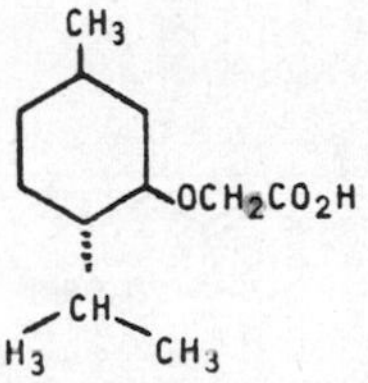

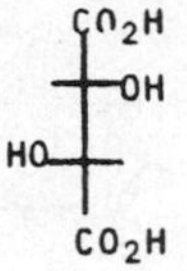

Reagents used to resolve neutral compounds:
    Alcohols: See problem 2c.
    Ketones/aldehydes:

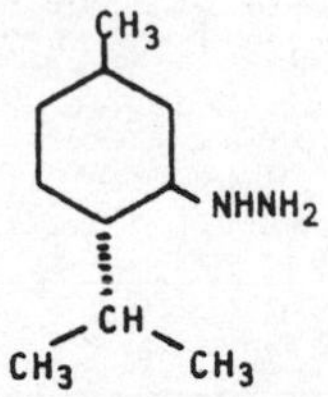

Menthylhydrazine 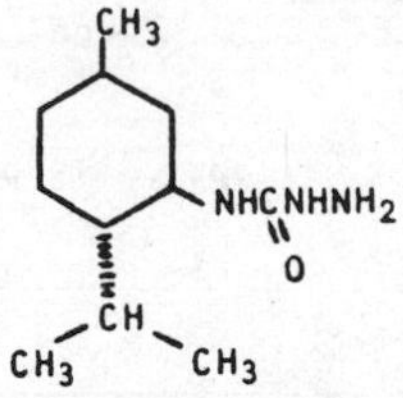   Menthylsemicarbazide

2. a.

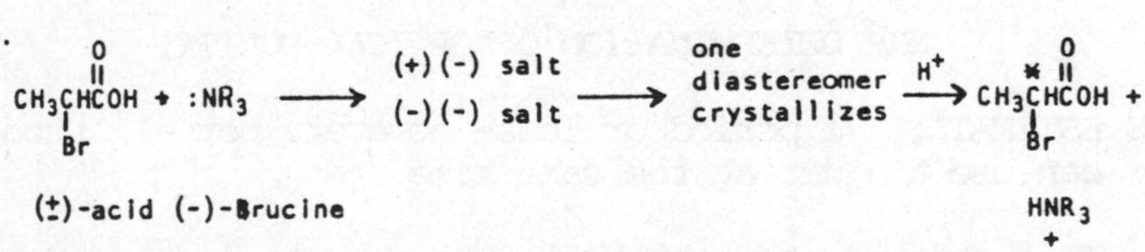

$$CH_3\overset{O}{\overset{\|}{C}HCOH} + :NR_3 \longrightarrow \begin{array}{l}(+)(-)\ salt\\(-)(-)\ salt\end{array} \longrightarrow \begin{array}{l}one\\diastereomer\\crystallizes\end{array} \xrightarrow{H^+} CH_3\overset{O}{\overset{\|}{C}HCOH} +$$

        |
        Br   Br

   (±)-acid (-)-Brucine   HNR$_3$
                                                                                                              +

187

b.

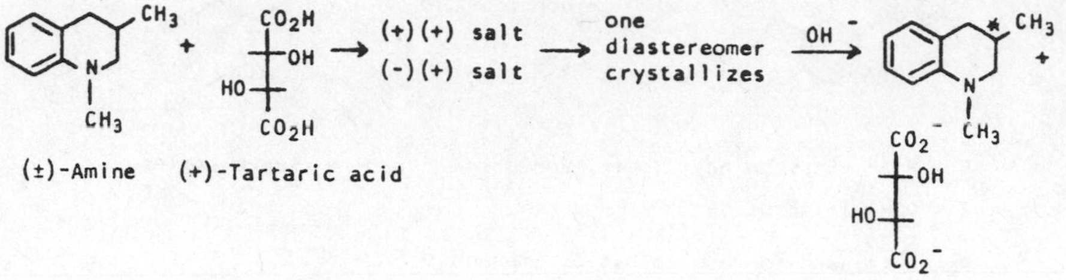

$(\pm)$-Amine   (+)-Tartaric acid

$(+)(+)$ salt → one diastereomer crystallizes → OH^- →

$(-)(+)$ salt

c.

$\underset{\text{($\pm$)-Alcohol}}{\underset{|}{\overset{CH_3}{PhCHOH}}}$ +

→

$\underset{(\pm)}{\overset{\displaystyle \overset{O}{\|}}{C-OH}}$, $\underset{CH_3}{\overset{|}{CO_2CHPh}}$

$(-)$-Brucine $(+)(-)$ salt
$(-)(-)$ salt

one diastereomer crystallizes

$\underset{\text{optically pure}}{\overset{\displaystyle \overset{O}{\|}}{C-OH}}$, $\underset{CH_3}{\overset{|}{CO_2CHPh}}$ *

$\xleftarrow{H^+}$

$\underset{*}{\underset{|}{\overset{CH_3}{PhCHOH}}}$ $\xleftarrow[\text{Heat}]{H^+/H_2O}$

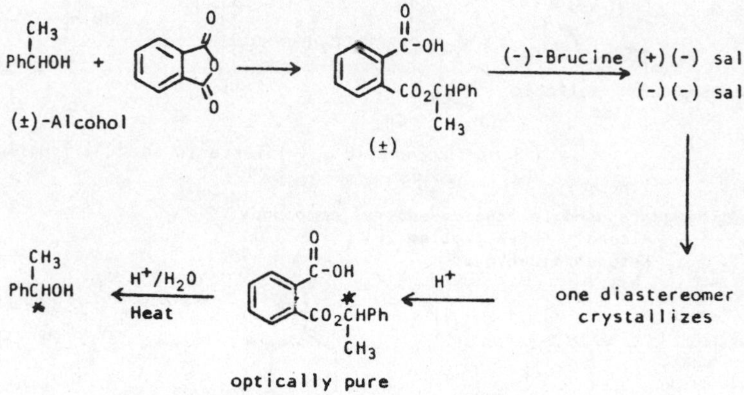

Experiment 62

NMR DETERMINATION OF OPTICAL PURITY

TIME ESTIMATE: 1 period or less- however, not all students can use the nmr at the same time.

This experiment might better be done as a class demonstration, giving all students a photocopy of the resulting spectra, so that they might determine percentages.

CHEMICALS PER 10 STUDENTS:

Nmr Tubes   10

Chloroform-d, 99.8 atom %, 0.03 % v/v TMS,   10 g
    Aldrich 22, 578-9

Tris[3-(heptafluoropropylhydroxymethylene)-(+)-   0.3 g
    camphorato], europium (III): [Eu(hfc)$_3$],
    Aldrich 16, 474-7. On page 500, this
    compound is named as tris(heptafluorobutyrl-
    d-camphorato) europium (III): [Eu(hfbc)$_3$].
    They are the same compound.

The resolved α-phenylethylamine from Experiment 61
    should be used.

Technique 3

CRYSTALLIZATION: THE PURIFICATION OF SOLIDS

ANSWERS TO PROBLEMS:

1. a. A plot similar to line A in Figure 3-1 on page 522
will be obtained. The line will be slightly curved.

    b. All of the substance A would dissolve at 80°. A
solubility of 17.0 g in 100 mL of water is equivalent to a
solubility of 0.85 g in 5 mL of water. This is a greater
solubility than is required.

    c. Crystals of A should appear around 56°C.

    d. The recovery of A would amount to 0.425 g. A solubi-
lity of 1.5 g in 100 mL of water at 0°C is equivalent to a
solubility of 0.075 g in 5 mL of water. Therefore, 0.075 g of
A would remain dissolved in the water, with the remainder
being formed as crystals.

2. If a saturated hot solution were filtered by vacuum filtration, the cooling which occurred as the solvent was drawn
through the filter paper would cause the solute to precipitate
in the form of crystals. The result would be that the filter
paper would become clogged with crystals, and impurities would
not be removed successfully from the solution being filtered.

3. a.   b.

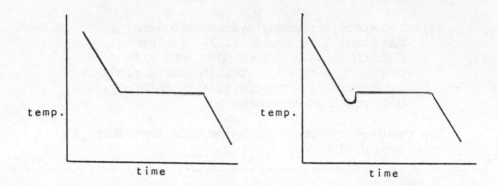

4. a. Add 100 mL of boiling water to the mixture, remove the
insoluble B by gravity filtration while the solution is hot,
and allow the filtrate to cool to 25° or less. If the solution is cooled to 25°, 1 g of A will remain in solution and 9
g of A will precipitate in the form of crystals. The crystals
are collected by vacuum filtration.

     b. Add 100 mL of boiling water to the mixture in order to
dissolve both A and B. Allow the mixture to cool to 25° or
below and collect the crystals. Since the solvent is capable
of holding as much as 1 g of impurity B, and since the amount
of B is much less than 1 g, no B will crystallize at 25°. The
crystals which form are those of pure A, which is collected by
vacuum filtration.

     c. For the first crystallization, add 100 mL of boiling
water. Allow the solution to cool to 25°. The solid which
precipitates will contain 9 g of A and 2 g of B. The solution
will contain 1 g of A and 1 g of B. For the second crystallization, 90 mL of hot water are required. When this solution
is cooled to 25°, the solid which precipitates will contain
8.1 g of A and 1.1 g of B. The remaining solution will
contain 0.9 g of A and 0.9 g of B. For the third crystallization, 81 mL of hot water are required. When this solution is
cooled, the solid which precipitates will contain 7.29 g of A
and 0.29 g of B. The remaining solution will contain 0.81 g
of A and 0.81 g of B. For the fourth crystallization, 72.9 mL
of hot water are required. When this solution is cooled, the
mother liquor will be capable of holding 0.729 g of A and
0.729 g of B. Since this amount of B is greater than the
amount of B left in the solid, no B will precipitate during

this fourth crystillization. The crystals of pure A will weigh 6.561 g. This purification sequence required four crystallizations. From the 10 g of A which were taken initially, 6.561 g were recovered. This corresponds to a percent recovery of 65.61%.

EXTRACTION, THE SEPARATORY FUNNEL,
DRYING AGENTS

ANSWERS TO PROBLEMS:

1.   Following the method given on pages 543 and 544, we obtain:

First extraction:

$$K = 1.0 = \frac{C_2}{C_1} = \left(\frac{\dfrac{5.0-x}{25} \quad \dfrac{g}{mL \ ether}}{\dfrac{x}{100} \quad \dfrac{g}{mL \ H_2O}}\right)$$

$$1.0 = \frac{(5.0-x)(100)}{25x}$$

$$25x = 500 - 100x$$

$$125x = 500$$

$$x = 4.0 \ g \ remaining \ in \ aqueous \ phase$$

Second extraction:

$$K = 1.0 = \frac{\left(\dfrac{4.0-x}{25} \quad \dfrac{g}{mL \ ether}\right)}{\left(\dfrac{x}{100} \quad \dfrac{g}{mL \ H_2O}\right)}$$

$$1.0 = \frac{(4.0-x)(100)}{25x}$$

$$25x = 400 - 100x$$

$$125x = 400$$

$$x = 3.20 \ g \ remaining \ in \ aqueous \ phase$$

$$5.0-x = 1.80 \ g \ extracted \ into \ ether \ phase$$

For one 50 mL extraction:

$$K = 1.0 = \frac{\left(\dfrac{5.0-x}{50} \ \dfrac{g}{mL \ ether}\right)}{\left(\dfrac{x}{100} \ \dfrac{g}{mL \ H_2O}\right)}$$

$$1.0 = \frac{(5.0-x)(100)}{50x}$$

$$50x = 500 - 100x$$

$$150x = 500$$

$$x = 3.33 \ g \ remaining \ in \ aqueous \ phase$$

$$5.0-x = 1.67 \ g \ extracted \ into \ ether \ phase$$

2.   This question may be answered using the procedures from a wide variety of possible experiments. However, separation schemes have been illustrated in this instructor's manual for Experiments 10 and 30, and for the isolation Experiments 5, 6, and 8. A separation scheme for Experiment 1 appears on page 17 of the textbook, itself.

Technique 6

BOILING POINTS, SIMPLE DISTILLATION,
AND VACUUM DISTILLATION

ANSWERS TO PROBLEMS:

1.   a.   290°

     b.   185°

     c.   155–165°

2.   T = 205°

$t_1 = 0°$

$$(0.000154)(205°)(205-35°) = 5.4° \ correction$$

$$Corrected \ b.p. = 205+5 = 210°$$

$t_2 = 35°$

3.   a. $PV = \dfrac{g}{m.w.} \ Rt; \quad g = \dfrac{PV \ (m.w.)}{RT} =$

$$\frac{(1 \ atm)(1 \ liter)(58 \ g/mole)}{(0.082)(273+56°)} = 2.15 \ g$$

192

b. $\dfrac{(1 \text{ atm})(0.05 \text{ liter})(58 \text{ g/mole})}{(0.082)(329°)} = 0.11 \text{ g}$

c. $\dfrac{2.15 \text{ g}}{15.0 \text{ g}}$ X 100 = 14.3% loss using 1 liter flask

$\dfrac{0.11 \text{ g}}{15.0 \text{ g}}$ X 100 = 0.73% loss using 50 mL flask

The smaller flask yields a better recovery of acetone.

Technique 7

FRACTIONAL DISTILLATION, AZEOTROPES

ANSWERS TO PROBLEMS:

1. a. 39 g = 0.5 mole benzene; 46 g = 0.5 mole toluene

$N_{C_6H_6} = \dfrac{0.5}{0.5+0.5} = 0.5$; $N_{C_7H_8} = 0.5$

   b. Partial vapor pressure of benzene = (270 mm) (0.5) = 135 mm

   c. At 90°, P_{total} = (1010 mm) (0.5) + (405 mm) (0.5) = 707 mm

   at 100°, P_{total} = (1340 mm) (0.5) + (560 mm) (0.5) = 950 mm

The boiling point is greater than 90°, but less than 100°. Assume a linear relationship between the vapor pressure of each substance and the temperature from 90 to 100°.

For benzene; $\dfrac{2}{10}$ (1340-1010) = 66 mm change in vapor pressure for each 2° change in temperature

For toluene; $\dfrac{2}{10}$ (560-405) = 31 mm change in vapor pressure for each 2° change in temperature

The following approximate vapor pressures are obtained at certain temperatures:

193

	benzene	toluene
90°	1010	405
92°	1076	436
94°	1142	467
96°	1208	498
98°	1274	529
100°	1340	560

At 92°; P_{total} = (1076)(0.5) + (436)(0.5) = 756 mm

Thus, the boiling point is approximately 92°.

d. Partial vapor pressure of benzene at 92° =

(1076)(0.5) = 538 mm

Partial vapor pressure of toluene at 92° =

(436)(0.5) = 218 mm

Vapor composition: $\frac{538}{760}$ = 0.71 benzene, 0.29

toluene

e. 0.71 mole = 55.4 g benzene; 0.29 mole = 26.7 g

toluene

$\frac{55.4 \text{ g}}{55.4 + 26.7 \text{ g}}$ X 100 = 67.5% benzene; 32.5% toluene

2. Three theoretical plates are needed.

3. a. P_{total} = P° $_{H_2O}$N$_{H_2O}$ + P° $\cancel{sucrose}$N$\cancel{sucrose}$ =

(760 mm)(0.8) = 608 mm

b. 100°

c. Pure water

d. The temperature would be above 100°, and would rise

194

continuously during the distillation process.

4.   See the explanation given in Section 6.3 in Technique 6.

5.   The mole fractions and boiling point data are used to obtain the lower curve such as that shown in Figure 7.4. The upper curve (vapor composition) such as that shown in Figure 7.4 may be obtained by performing calculations similar to those given on page 571 for each mixture.

6.   The distillate will have the composition of the azeotrope (95.6% ethanol). As the distillation proceeds, the residue in the distillation flask will become richer in the higher boiling component (pure ethanol). When all of the water has been removed as the azeotrope, pure ethanol will distill.

7.

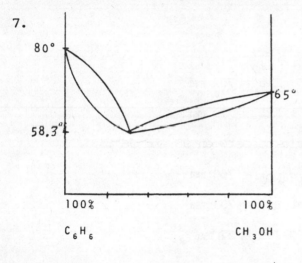

Mixture rich in benzene:
    The azeotrope dis-
    tills, and benzene
    concentrates in the
    distillation flask.

Mixture rich in metha-
nol:
    The azeotrope dis-
    tills, and methanol
    concentrates in the
    distillation flask.

8.

Mixture rich in
acetone:
    The acetone distills,
    and the azeotrope
    concentrates in the
    distillation flask.

Mixture rich in
chloroform:
    The chloroform dis-
    tills, and the azeo-
    trope concentrates in
    the distillation
    flask.

195

9. From Table 7-2, ten plates would be required to separate the mixture. From Table 7-3, a 80 cm column would be required (2.5 plates/20 column). The hold-up in the column would amount to 4 mL (1 mL/2.5 plates).

Technique 8
STEAM DISTILLATION
ANSWERS TO PROBLEMS:

1.
$$\frac{\text{Wt. benzene}}{\text{Wt. water}} = \frac{(P^\circ C_6H_6)(M.W.\ C_6H_6)}{(P^\circ H_2O)(M.W.\ H_2O)} = \frac{(760-227.7)(78)}{(227.7)(18)} = \frac{10.1\ g}{1\ g\ H_2O}$$

$$\frac{10.1\ g}{10.1\ +\ 1.0\ g} \times 100 = 91.0\%,\ 9.0\%\ \text{water}$$

Table 8-1 gives 8.9% water.

2. At 95°; P_{total} = 634 + 118 = 752 mm

At 96°; P_{total} = 657 + 122 = 779 mm

The boiling point would be between 95 and 96°.

3. P_{total} = 733 mm + $P_{C_6H_5NO_2}$ = 760 mm

v.p. H_2O at 99° = 733 mm

$P_{C_6H_5NO_2}$ = 760-733 = 27 mm

$$\frac{\text{Wt } C_6H_5NO_2}{\text{Wt water}} = \frac{(27)(123)}{(733)(18)} = \frac{0.25\ g\ C_6H_5NO_2}{1\ g\ water}$$

4. The o-nitrophenol has an internal hydrogen bond. Since p-nitrophenol cannot bond internally, it will hydrogen bond to water and will not co-distill (its vapor pressure is much lower than the ortho isomer because it is strongly associated with water molecules).

Technique 13

SUBLIMATION

ANSWERS TO PROBLEMS:

1.   Solid carbon dioxide passes directly from the solid state to the gaseous state. Since one does not observe a liquid, as with solid water, it is called "Dry Ice."

2.   At a pressure above 5.1 atm, one can have liquid carbon dioxide.

3.   As the temperature is raised, the vapor pressure of the solid increases. When this pressure equals the applied pressure (76 mm), it will sublime. One will not observe a solid to liquid transition (melting point).

4.   The solid will show a normal solid to liquid transition at 100°.

5.   When the applied pressure is reduced to a value equal to or below 50 mm, it will sublime upon heating to about 100°.

Technique 15

POLARIMETRY

ANSWERS TO QUESTIONS:

1. $[\alpha]_D^{25} = \dfrac{\alpha}{c\,\ell}$

$\alpha = -10°$
$c = 0.4$ g/mL
$\ell = 0.5$ dm

$[\alpha]_D^{25} = \dfrac{-10°}{(0.4)(0.5)}$

$= -50°$

2.   Observed specific rotation =

$$\dfrac{\text{optical purity x specific rotation of pure substance}}{100}$$

$$= \frac{(80)(+20)}{100}$$

$$= +16°$$

$\alpha = [\alpha]_D^{25} \, C\ell$ $c = 2.0 \text{ g/mL}$

$= (+16)(2.0)(2)$ $\ell = 2 \text{ dm}$

$= +64°$

3.   Optical purity $= \dfrac{\text{observed } [\alpha]}{[\alpha] \text{ of pure substance}} \times 100$

$= \dfrac{-8°}{-10°} \times 100$

$= 80\%$

The product contains:

% (–)-enantiomer $= \left[X + \left(\dfrac{100-X}{2} \right) \right] \%$ $X = $ optical purity

$= \left[80 + \dfrac{20}{2} \right]$

$= 90\%$

% (+)-enantiomer $= 100{-}90 = 10\%$

A SAMPLE SCHEDULE (AS USED BY THE AUTHORS)
FOR TWO TERMS OF 20 PERIODS EACH

FIRST QUARTER

PERIODS ALLOTTED	EXPERIMENT OR LECTURE	READING ASSIGNMENTS
1	LECTURE 1 Safety/Filtration CHECK-IN LECTURE 2 Crystallization	Forward to the Student, Laboratory Safety Techniques 1-4
2	Choice of EXP 1 Acetylsalicylic Acid EXP 2 Acetanilide EXP 3 Acetaminophen LECTURE 3 Notebooks/Reports/ Calculations	Advance Prepara- tion and Labora- tory Records, Laboratory Glass- ware
2	LECTURE 4 Extraction Choice of: EXP 5 Nicotine EXP 6 Caffeine from Tea EXP 7 Caffeine from Coffee	Techniques 5,6,13
2	LECTURE 5 Column Chromatography EXP 36 (Parts 4 and 6) Separa- tion of a Dye Mixture by TLC and Column Chromatography LECTURE 6 Thin Layer Chromato- graphy	Techniques 10,11
1	EXP 4 TLC Analysis of Analgesic Drugs LECTURE 7 Distillation - Part One	
2	LECTURE 8 Distillation - Part Two EXP 10 Isopentyl Acetate or EXP 9 Ethanol from Sucrose	Techniques 7,8

2	EXP 18 Essential Oils	
	MID-TERM EXAM	Technique 17
	LECTURE 9 Students are shown	(Infrared)
	how to use salt plates and to	
	operate the infrared spectrometer	

2	LECTURE 10 Gas Chromatography	
	Do both:	
	EXP 24 Nucleophilic Substitu-	
	tion: Competing Nucleophiles	Technique 12
	EXP 22 Reactivities of Alkyl	(Technique 16)
	Halides	

2	AROMATIC SUBSTITUTION EXPERIMENT
	EXP 31 Nitration of Methyl
	Benzoate
	or EXP 32 p-Nitroaniline
	or EXP 34 Methyl orange
	We vary these from year to year.

2	EXP 30 Grignard Reaction
	Choice of benzoic acid or
	triphenylmethanol
	LECTURE 11 Students are shown
	how to make a KBr pellet.

1	ALKENE ADDITION EXPERIMENT
	EXP 13 Methyl Stearate from
	Methyl Oleate (hydrogenation)
	or EXP 28 Addition of Dichloro-
	carbene to Cyclohexene via Phase
	Transfer Catalysis

1	EXP 55 Polymers (optional)
	CHECK-OUT

---

20 PERIODS + FINAL EXAMINATION

PERIODS ALLOTTED	EXPERIMENT	READING ASSIGNMENTS
1	EXP 56 Identification of Unknowns	
	Each student receives one solid and one liquid unknown after he or she completes the series of functional group tests on the suggested known compounds. Spectra are issued as soon as the student completes a probable identification of the unknown's functional groups based on solubilities and chemical classification tests. The unknowns are due at the end of the quarter. This first period is the only full period devoted to this experiment. Otherwise the student is expected to work on these unknowns whenever free time is available.	Experiment 56 Appendices 3,4
3	EXP 20 An Oxidation-Reduction Scheme: Borneol, Camphor, Isoborneol Use of the nmr is demonstrated	Technique 13 Technique 17 (NMR) Appendix 5
3	EXP 29 Markovnikov and anti-Markovnikov Hydration of Styrene Students should pair-up so that one student does hydroboration (EXP 29A) and the other does oxymercuration (EXP 29B)	Technique 12
2	EXP 21 Spearmint and Caraway Oils: (-) and (+)-Carvones Students work in pairs MID-TERM EXAM	Techniques 6,7 (review) Techniques 9,15, 16

201

3-4	MULTI-STEP SYNTHESIS	
	EXP 43 p-Aminobenzoic acid (PABA)	

	EXP 44 Benzocaine (optional -
	             test this drug on an ex-
	             cised frog's leg muscle)	

	EXP 38/39 Benzoin	
	EXP 40 Benzil	
or	EXP 46 Tetraphenylcyclopentadienone	
	EXP 51 Benzyne and Diels-Alder Reaction	

2-3	SPECIALIZED CHEMICAL REACTIONS	
	EXP 33 Friedel-Crafts Acylation	Techniques 6,9,17
	or	

	EXP 42 Sulfa Drugs
	       Choice of one drug with
	       optional testing on bacteria
		Appendices 3,4,5

	or	
	EXP 45 5-n-Butylbarbituric Acid	Techniques 6,9,14
	or	
	EXP 47 Enamine Reactions	Techniques 6,9
	or	
	EXP 48/49 Aldol Condensation and Dimedone	Technique 14
	or	
	EXP 50 Tetraphenylporphyrin/ Metallo derivatives	
	We vary these from year-to- year.	

2	EXP 61 Resolution of (+/-)-α- Phenylethylamine	Techniques 6,15

1	EXP 26 Chromic Acid Oxidation of Alcohols (Kinetics) This experiment uses a UV/Visible spectrophotometer. Students com- plete the experiment when the in- strument is available. Results are reported by the end of the quarter.

2	FINISH UNKNOWNS (EXP 56)
	CHECK-OUT

---

20 PERIODS + FINAL EXAMINATION

REACTION TYPE INDEX

$$tBuCl + H_2O \longrightarrow tBuOH$$

$$\underset{\underset{CH_3}{|}}{Ph-CH-Cl} + H_2O \longrightarrow \underset{\underset{CH_3}{|}}{Ph-CH-OH}$$

    (The above experiment also includes preparation of the chlorides.)

EXPERIMENTS SUITABLE FOR THE FIRST
INTRODUCTION TO A TECHNIQUE

FILTRATION/CRYSTALLIZATION/MELTING POINT

EXP 1	Aspirin
EXP 2	Acetanilide
EXP 3	Acetaminophen
EXP 8	Cholesterol from Gallstones
EXP 12	Hydrolysis of Methyl Salicylate
EXP 31	Nitration of Methyl Benzoate

HEATING UNDER SIMPLE REFLUX

EXP 6	Isolation of Caffeine from Tea
EXP 7	Isolation of Caffeine from Coffee
EXP 10	Isopentyl Acetate (Banana Oil)
EXP 12	Hydrolysis of Methyl Salicylate

EXTRACTION/THE SEPARATORY FUNNEL/DRYING AGENTS

EXP 5	Nicotine from Tobacco
EXP 6	Isolation of Caffeine from Tea
EXP 7	Isolation of Caffeine from Coffee

SIMPLE DISTILLATION

EXP 9	Ethanol from Sucrose (also includes a fractional distillation)
EXP 10	Isopentyl Acetate (Banana Oil)
EXP 23A	n-Butyl Bromide
EXP 23B	t-Pentyl Chloride
EXP 27	Cyclohexene

VACUUM DISTILLATION/MANOMETERS

EXP 11	Methyl Salicylate (Oil of Wintergreen)
EXP 16	N,N-Diethyl-m-toluamide
EXP 21	Spearmint and Caraway Oils (actually a vacuum fractional distillation)
EXP 33	Friedel-Crafts Acylation
EXP 45	5-n-Butylbarbituric Acid
EXP 47	Enamine Reactions

FRACTIONAL DISTILLATION

> EXP 9   Ethanol from Sucrose
> EXP 21   Spearmint and Caraway Oils
>   (actually a vacuum fractional distillation,
>   and also includes gas chromatography and
>   polarimetry)

AZEOTROPIC DISTILLATION

> EXP 47   Enamine Reactions

STEAM DISTILLATION

> EXP 18   Essential Oils from Spices

COLUMN CHROMATOGRAPHY

> EXP 36   Chromatography of Some Dye Mixtures (Part VI)
> EXP 37   Carotenoid Pigments from Spinach
> EXP 16   N,N-Diethyl-m-toluamide

THIN LAYER CHROMATOGRAPHY

> EXP 14   TLC Analysis of Analgesic Drugs
> EXP 19   Oxidation of Borneol to Camphor
> EXP 32   p-Nitroaniline
> EXP 36   Chromatography of Some Dye Mixtures (Part IV)

PAPER CHROMATOGRAPHY

> EXP 36   Chromatography of Food Colors (Part I)
> EXP 60   Paper Chromatography of Amino Acids

GAS CHROMATOGRAPHY

> EXP 17   Gas Chromatographic Analysis of Gasolines
> EXP 24   Nucleophilic Substitution Reactions:
>   Competing Nucleophiles
> EXP 21   Spearmint and Caraway Oils
> EXP 29   Hydration of Styrene

SUBLIMATION

> EXP 6   Isolation of Caffeine from Tea
> EXP 7   Isolation of Caffeine from Coffee

EXP 20   An Oxidation-Reduction Scheme:
          Borneol, Camphor, Isoborneol

HANDLING SODIUM METAL

    EXP 45   5-n-Butylbarbituric Acid
    EXP 49   5,5-dimethyl-1,3-cyclohexanedione (Dimedone)

POLARIMETRY

    EXP 21   Spearmint and Caraway Oils
    EXP 59   Mutarotation of Lactose
    EXP 61   Resolution of (+/-)-α-Phenylethylamine

REFRACTOMETRY

    EXP 21   Spearmint and Caraway Oils
    EXP 24   Nucleophilic Substitution Reactions:
              Competing Nucleophiles

PHASE TRANSFER CATALYSIS

    EXP 28   Addition of Dichlorocarbene to Cyclohexene

CATALYTIC HYDROGENATION

    EXP 13   Methyl Stearate from Methyl Oleate

SPECTROSCOPY

    INFRARED SPECTROSCOPY

        This technique may be introduced almost anywhere,
    however, experiments which specifically incorporate the
    use of infrared spectroscopy in a special fashion are:

    EXP 18   Essential Oils from Spices
    EXP 20   An Oxidation-Reduction Scheme:
              Borneol, Camphor, Isoborneol
    EXP 21   Spearmint and Caraway Oils
    EXP 33   Friedel-Crafts Acylation
    EXP 56   Identification of Unknowns

NMR SPECTROSCOPY

        This technique may be introduced almost anywhere,
    however, experiments which involve a special use of nmr

218

spectroscopy (for instance, quantitative analysis)
include:

EXP 18   Essential Oils from Spices
EXP 20   An Oxidation-Reduction Scheme:
            Borneol, Camphor, Isoborneol (proton and
            carbon)
EXP 21   Spearmint and Caraway Oils
EXP 24   Nucleophilic Substitution Reactions:
            Competing Nucleophiles
EXP 33   Friedel-Crafts Acylation (proton and carbon)
EXP 56   Identification of Unknowns